Americans love to hate immigrants. Italians, Irish or Asian and Arabic, it doesn't matter. We love them when they pick our crops. We hate them when they take away our jobs.

We love them when they produce and pay taxes. We hate them when they fill the welfare rolls.

We love them when they die in service to our country. We hate them when they demand equal status with Americans that settled here before them.

Then came September 11, 2001.

Will we close our borders? Should we shut out the best and brightest from other countries, eager to thrive in the light of freedom, capitalism and democracy?

This true story is about one Italian family. Like Peter in the garden of Gethsemane with Christ, Marcello D'Alessandro sinned three times. Yet in one generation, he produced a hero of World War II, a productive, tax-paying citizen, and a capitalist. The world is a better place because of the progeny of Marcello D'Alessandro.

Throughout our history, we've demonstrated schizophrenia to those outside our shores and borders. Be it the first great wave of English and Irish, the second great wave of Italian and Greeks, or the present day influx of Mexicans and Asians, we Americans are of two minds. Love them for what they give. Hate them for what they take. Especially if they take from me.

In this state of turmoil our country endures today, Marcello's actions and that of his family are instructive. Perhaps we Americans will use them as a template to deal with today's immigration question.

Bastion of freedom?

Or isolationist withdrawal.

Each citizen must choose. Choose wisely.

RESEARCHING YOUR FAMILY

There are many resources available. Each captain by law filled out a ship's manifest during the height of turn of the century immigration. The manifest listed port of debarkation, name, and home village. The Catholic Church in Italy kept extensive records of the Sacraments. The Italian bureaucracy recorded taxes, births and deaths.

In the US, a census is taken every ten years. It collects demographic information from everyone counted.

Don't forget to search the Ellis Island directory of immigrants.

Also look for help with your family's genealogy at

www.ancestry.com
www.familysearch.org
www.familytreemaker.com
www.genealogy.com

A TRIO OF LIES

The True Story of passion, betrayal and triumph in our Italian family.

By Frank Barry

4

Printed in the United States of America by Pikes Peak Publishing. Garamond type First printing May, 2002

ISBN 0-9719654-0-4

ABOUT THE AUTHOR

Frank Barry is married to Mary D'Alessandro. After years of oral history, he undertook this labor of love to document the incredible events of the D'Alessandro family. The lessons learned couldn't be more relevant since the tragedy of September 11, 2001.

His profession is a Medical Doctor in Colorado Springs, Colorado. His passion lies in finding stories of interest to all, and telling them in a compelling manner.

Previous works include non-fiction books *Make the Change for a Healthy Heart* and *The Healthy Heart Formula*, published by John Wiley.

Look for his first novel, China Lives!

During his childhood in Jersey City, New Jersey, he gazed over the Hudson River towards Ellis Island, the docks lining the river, and the Western Jersey Railroad terminal, never realizing the stories they held. Visiting Ellis Island as an adult, he experienced the power of those cataclysmic days. He captured their hopes and heartbreak in the story that follows.

ACKNOWLEDGEMENTS

The true detective work for this book belongs to Janet Andrews D'Alessandro. With her usual focused determination, she uncovered the layers of time and deceit that hid our nuclear family from their relatives. Without her discoveries, there would be no material for this book. Dave Howes, Janet's husband, contributed the digital photography enclosed. Thank you for great art, Dave.

To our new-found Italian relatives, who personify the attributes of love, passion and prowess at cooking, thank you for sharing the European perspective on life and living.

I'd be nowhere without the dedication and support of my family. Mary, Colleen and Megan, thank you.

Credit also belongs to numerous librarians and researchers in New York, San Francisco and New Jersey without whose work we'd be doomed to repeat past mistakes.

Charles Andrews and his wife Ceil personify American attitudes of hard work, love of family and generosity. Losing my parents at a young age, I've been privileged to know them for the last twenty-two years. Thank you for your love.

Frank Barry, 2002

CONTENTS

ILLUSTRATIONS

GRANDMA

1926- Visitacion Valley, San Francisco

"Putana," he screamed. "Putana! Capisce?"

Not again.. Elizabeth's thoughts percolated to consciousness from deep inside her head. Not another meaningless argument. Why did he do this to her? She fulfilled his every desire and fantasy. She left her babies for him. She still loved him. Why did he despise her?

The door slammed. Elizabeth forced her eyes open. The pounding headache made her vision blur. Again, for the millionth time, she saw her home: tattered curtains, soiled throw rug near the door, worn furniture in the kitchen. Everything worn down. Eyes heavy, her gaze wandered over her domain, from vegetable garden in the back yard to small lawn of green grass in the front, beyond the porch. Perhaps she'd sit on the front porch later and cool off. Anything to escape the unbearable headache.

His constant screaming made her shake. They didn't fight. That takes two. When Frank flew into a rage, calling her horrible things, threatening her, he tore her heart. She didn't understand why. Like a good Italian woman, she obeyed. His authority remained unquestioned. It made her weak with fear just to think about his screaming.

She sat in her favorite living room chair. The shaking wouldn't stop. It was a long time since she felt anything. Now, today, only numbness, an abyss. She didn't feel human any more. A person shouldn't have to suffer like this. A person has dignity, a soul, and an angel to watch over her. She had only pain.

How long since she'd been happy? She couldn't remember.

Coughing racked her thin body. The influenza terrorized San Francisco. The doctor said she was run down, suffering from nervous exhaustion. A long string of minor illnesses, the doctor repeated. Elizabeth felt like a boulder sat on her chest. She lost weight, couldn't eat. Sleep wouldn't come. Fear overwhelmed her.

She prayed.

She cried bitter tears. What became of her didn't matter. What about the children? What about those left behind? Would Frank care for them? Or would they be discarded on the trash heap of life to fend for themselves?

Elizabeth grew too tired to think. She needed relief. Sleep didn't restore her. Food had no taste. Even the air she breathed failed to sustain her spirit. She felt like a candle put under a glass. Burning brightly, it slowly, ever so slowly lost its light. Finally, with a puff of energy, it burned out, lost in blackness, never to shine again. Only a pitiful trail of smoke, curling upwards, marked its very essence. Extinguished.

She could not bear another fight with Frank. Arms clenched, fists waving, he called her names, shouted obscene words, degraded her. Tears came as she remembered the worst part- the children heard every word. At least the three who were here. What of the others? Did they too hear? All her babies gone, how very sad. Her children hearing the verbal abuse worsened the degradation.

Relief.

The thought skittered along the margins of her distressed brain. She walked to the tiny kitchen. Spying a stain on the sink, Elizabeth mechanically opened the cupboard and grasped the Lysol. Spilling a drop on the stain, she rubbed and rubbed till it was no more. Just what I need, she thought, to rub my sins away till they are no more. She murmured an Ave Maria.

She looked away to no avail. Her hand worked on its own, separated from her mind. It grasped the Lysol bottle. Her mouth opened and she drank deeply. Searing pain in her throat registered on one hidden level of her mottled psyche, not rising to consciousness. Drinking again, it coursed down her gullet, burning everything in its path. A third time she drank, till the bottle emptied and it fell from the robotic hand.

Frank will be coming home soon, she thought, why don't I sit on the front porch and wait for him.

Then came darkness.

The neighbors noticed her passed out on the porch at 5:30 PM on this sunny Tuesday. She did not have a drinking habit. Her behavior drew a crowd of concerned friends. Frank walked down Cora Street, wondering out loud what happened. He remained the master of his universe, expecting his dinner on the table. As he watched, her tiny body writhed, contracted with the fierce electrical discharges of her dying brain, then relaxed into abnormal repose. Frank held her head. He and the neighbor called the ambulance. Her pale skin blanched, then a semblance of color returned.

They discovered the empty bottle.

Ambulance lights and cacophony of sound alerted those not already in attendance. The ambulance crew, wiser than their age suggested, bundled her onto the stretcher and allowed Frank to travel with them. They arrived at Mission Emergency Hospital within minutes. They shook their heads to the chief nurse. Not much hope for this one.

Wild swings of metabolism caused her heart to speed and slow. The corrosive Lysol poisoned her kidneys, affected the lung's ability to bring air and oxygen to her exhausted tissues. She repeated the spasms, now longer and forceful, pulling her away from her pain, pulling her towards the relief of eternity.

The doctor did the best she could. Placing the tube down the throat, it slid through the burn in the stomach, along with the Lysol. Nothing returned as she applied suction. Nothing to pump out. In five minutes, her heart slowed. Breath came in wisps. Finally, her heart stopped.

Death, at last.

Frank hung his head in shame. How could she do this to him?

The inquest report became a matter of public record: Cardiac arrest due to Lysol poisoning. A suicide. Age 35. Left behind three children and a husband.

Life goes on.

How very sad.

A

CHAPTER ONE

DISCOVERY

March, 1999- San Francisco

You can't go home again.

That phrase doesn't describe Janet. She never left. Strong ties bind her to the Andrews family. She lives a short ride away from parents' and sisters. Her dental practice sits between her parent's house and the house the family first owned. Like a good Italian, she loves to visit relatives and partake of important events- Christenings, marriages, funerals.

Family comes first.

She's always been crazy about family. When they cut, she bleeds. She lives for them, to visit, share meals and stress and experiences. When she found out about her grandmother's suicide, it came as quite a blow. The details were a well-kept family secret. Why did Elizabeth do it?

She wondered if it were catching, a hidden genetic trait she shared. Perhaps the times, stressful, fraught with danger, drove her to protest life itself. Were Janet's five sisters, grandma's offspring, so different?

As a child, Janet's extended family consisted of the maternal Irish side. Mom, Cecelia Cull, kept in close touch with her sister and her five children. They grew up together as one big family. When a dinner table sat ten or twelve, Janet felt at home. Eating alone made her lonely. She might miss something. The more people, the more fun, and with it came that feeling of security.

Their father, a retired businessman and veteran of World War II and the Great Depression, came from a small family, a brother and sister. Growing up, Janet saw them frequently. Granddad died when she was young. Why didn't she know the rest of the Italian side?

Why didn't Janet hear about her grandmother's tragedy sooner? Janet had to discover the true reason. She needed answers. Grandmother's shocking death started her quest.

The relatives couldn't be that hard to find.

Janet set out on her quest. She'd never lacked tenacity. She refused to be discouraged by international travel, mysterious twists, or frustrating dead ends. The quest grew into more than she imagined. Ultimately she grew to celebrate her lost side. She's gratified to learn the origins and sacrifices these relatives made to live, sometimes just to survive.

It's strange, comparing generations.

As a Baby Boomer, Janet's generation lived through Viet Nam, the assassination of President Kennedy, the Nixon years and Woodstock. They were the landmarks by which the Baby Boomer generation judges life. How do they compare with the sacrifices of ancient Italian relatives?

Truly, things were different then. War, famine, depression, social upheaval were not a part of her Baby Boomer generation experience. How would she have coped?

She'd find out on the trip.

"Last call for United Flight 600 to Rome. Non-stop service from San Francisco to Frankfurt, then direct to Rome."

Janet felt her blood pressure rising watching the towers of the Golden Gate bridge peak above the clouds. Traffic trapped her on Highway 101 near San Francisco Airport. Takeoff approached. Her stress rose.

The trip caused terrific strain. She spent hours with the travel agent working on the itinerary for five sisters and her parents. More time coordinating with the relatives in Italy. After the bulk of her work was complete, she forgot a translator. That set her off on another mission that ended with hiring a professional tour guide and translator, Sandra Di Domizio, the Backroads Italian Regional Coordinator. They'd rendezvous at the airport in the Eternal City of Rome. Janet had one more obstacle. Get on the plane. Preferably before it took off.

Running to the gate, she boarded as the attendants announced last call. "I made it."

Shouting the greeting, she slumped into her seat on the Boeing 747. She took a breath of air to relax. Her sisters surrounded her in the crowded compartment.

Peggy, the eldest, a successful businesswoman in Burlingame, Califorbaptized him Catholic. He'd trained as a Presbyterian all his adult life! Ceil was happy about that little bit of news. Today, the day after their anniversary party, they journeyed to a unique reunion. They'd meet the family.

As the plane settled into flight and the seatbelt sign went off, Peggy asked, "What started all this, Janet? Why did you spend hundred's of hours looking into dad's heritage?"

Janet threw a pillow at her. "It's all your fault. When you visited mom's Irish relatives in Kilkeel, it got me thinking about the other half. You know how I identify with dad. I always look up to him in everything I do. We're so much alike. Although mom was cuddlier, dad gave me the drive, motivation and direction to make something of my life. The morals and ideals I have spring from his work ethic and sense of value. He's always looked at the big picture and helped me get through the details. He taught me to become a useful, productive citizen. I'm sure that's why he's been so successful. It worked for me."

Elaine nodded. "You and dad are so alike, it's scary."

"My breast cancer motivated me, too. Those years of treatment and uncertainty were incredibly hard. I struggled to figure out who I was and where I belonged. Fight to the bitter end? Or submit to whatever was in store? I found my life had meaning and substance I hadn't realized prior to my illness. My cure forced me to ponder my beginnings. I determined to find my place in the family history. It's a labor of love. All these new people and places felt friendly, like family. It's given me a sense of belonging."

"Go on, tell us more," Peggy said.

"Getting started was easy. I knew dad's name was originally D'Alessandro, and his father came from Italy on the boat as an immigrant passing through Ellis Island. The rest was a struggle. To tell the truth, it's been fun. That's why I'm so thrilled about this trip. I've got high expectations, especially after corresponding with Domenico these last months. I want this meeting to be perfect, a storybook ending as well as a beginning. I couldn't sleep last night."

"Janet," Nancy asked, "what have you discovered about our new relatives?"

"They're great, kind, loving people."

"On the map, Southern Italy looks mountainous and isolated. Do they still farm, or have they moved to other work?"

"They farm an experimental form of wheat called Grano Duro, used to make pasta. They garden and raise olive trees. Domenico also has a diesel gasoline business."

"Do they make their own wine?"

"Yes, they make their own wine from local grapes grown in their own vineyards. I'll enjoy some of that this trip." She'd planned every detail.

Ceil Andrews sat down next to her children. "Janet, let me tell them about the breakthrough in the family research. It came the day of Janet's first contact with the Italian relatives. It happened like this…"

"Dr. Andrews, telephone call for Dr. Andrews."

Janet finished with her patient Mrs. Trainor. She completed extensive dental work, and this was the last visit. "Thanks so much for all your help, doctor. I feel great about what you've done. How was your recent vacation?"

Janet removed the gloves and mask. "Disappointing. You know, Mrs. Trainor, I hoped to contact my Italian relatives. I've been tracking the family tree for over two years, and I wanted this to be the breakthrough. But Dave and I came up short. We traveled to Basilicata province in southern Italy. Try as we might, we couldn't make the right contacts. I left my business cards at the inn, just in case. We enjoyed the biking and wine and food, but I feel hollow inside. I wanted to expand the family again. As children, we played with each other, your daughter and our five cousins. Everyone brought a friend to dinner on the weekend. If there wasn't a crowd it was too quiet, almost spooky. Our family is one big, happy crowd, and we feel comfortable that way. It gives us a sense of security and a greater feeling of belonging."

"Dr. Andrews, your call is waiting."

"Excuse me, Mrs. Trainor. I'll see you in a month. I need to answer this call. Hi to Mary Ellen."

"Janet, it's from Italy!"

Janet spoke into the telephone in broken Italian. "Hello, Pronto! May I help you?"

"It's Domenico Annunziata, from Calciano, Italy. We received your card from the innkeeper. I drove four hours, trying to overtake you before you left. We are the ones you look for. We are your Italian family!"

Ceil smiled. "Knowing the new relatives, she learned about the old. Janet, tell them about the pivotal day in our family history."

Janet shook her head. "Not yet. Let me set the stage. The beginnings of our clan in Italy allowed me to grasp what transpired. Knowing the family history, you'll understand why we never knew our Italian relatives."

A

CHAPTER TWO

THE OLD COUNTRY

Southern Italy, 1840's. Five generations past, before Italy unified.

"In nomine Patre, et Filei, et Spiritue Sancte. Amen." The young priest looked over his congregation, starting Mass in the chilly church with the sign of the Cross. Newly ordained by the Bishop, his words and gestures demonstrated training, belief and above all respect for this most precious of Catholic traditions. The old church building, simple yet elegant, like the Christ child of Christmas, remained a fitting stage for the rite. Stone, stucco and whitewash lent a solemn air to the events inside. The priest carried the burden of the Church of Christ on his shoulders. He was too new to carry the burdens of the villagers. That would come in the fullness of time.

Giovanni D'Alessandro demonstrated his love of the Catholic Church. He sat in respectful silence with his fellow farmers. A full head of black hair, olive skin, and dark eyes, his entire being intent on the sacrament. Dressed in traditional dark hat, jacket, white shirt and dark trousers of his village, the gravity of the Mass affected him. He loved the ceremony, the unchanging sameness, and the transfiguration of the wine and bread into the body and blood of Our Lord Jesus Christ. Wine, and especially its transformation in the sacrament, held special meaning for Giovanni. Praying in Church gave him great comfort and solace from the realities of life outside. His wife prayed beside him, her head covered in a shawl, holding their little girl. The cool

October breeze of the autumn outside did not disturb their Mass. Mass gave him special comfort today, a remarkable day for his family.

A slight man, years of backbreaking labor on the farm hardened Giovanni's muscles. Sun exposure turned his skin almost as dark as his hair and eyes. The long nose marked him of southern Italian roots. Giovanni never complained of his station in life. He had enough to eat, made the traditional Italian *sfuso* (loose wine) to drink, and enjoyed the love of his wife. This special day, ecstasy turned his thoughts from prayer.

Angelantonia of Avia, his wife of several years, would soon present him with another child. Barely twenty-five years old, she too was content with her life. Childbearing, rearing, herding the goats, cooking and all the other duties and responsibilities of a good wife she took in stride. How proud she was of her strength and youthful good looks. Her husband and other men of the village turned their heads when she approached. Age and work had not broken her spirit. She cheerfully fulfilled the expectations of her husband, and now thanked God for the opportunity that she desperately wished, to present him with a boy.

They didn't know they were poor.

Their options didn't seem limiting in this year of Our Lord 1844. A full day of labor, food enough, folk festivals and Church for prayer and spiritual guidance occupied their lives. The priest gave them succor. Giovanni and Angelantonia enjoyed their region and village. The outside world didn't interest them. Transportation in their Basilicata district of southern Italy consisted of the occasional horse and hiking along the thin, winding mountain paths between villages. Where else would they go?

Generations of families lived in this same mountainous district, longer than anyone could remember. If they wished to see the great ocean, they had only to travel down the river to the Gulf of Taranto on the Ionian Sea. Transcontinental or trans-oceanic travel was not possible. Why not consider a flight to the moon?

After the Consecration, the couple lined up for the privilege of Communion. He with chest thrust out, she with belly bursting, they received the thin wafer and bowed their heads in prayer. Giovanni listened to the Latin phrases, the sacramental ritual. The Church, like their lives, never changed. The thought satisfied Giovanni.

The priest intoned *"Ita Missa est."* (Go, the Mass is ended.)

Everything was as it should be, perfectly as expected. They strolled arm in arm to mingle with their fellow *Contadini* (illiterate peasants), trading snippets of gossip or information on crops. On Sundays, the Church remained a focal point for socializing. Easier work days, Sundays required only limited chores to perform. The relaxation of Sunday felt a contrast to the other days of the week, as Giovanni's hours filled with long hard tasks of tilling, pruning, weeding and praying for sufficient rain.

Giovanni couldn't contain his enthusiasm. After gossip with the neighbors, his wife spoke with the priest about the upcoming birth and Baptism. Giovanni's thoughts drifted. What changes he lived through in his twenty-eight years!

Since his birth in 1816, he remembered his father Guiseppe's stories about Napoleon Bonaparte, Emperor of France. Late at night, or during the Saint's feast days, his father regaled the boy with Napoleon's military victories. Napoleon was crowned King of Italy in 1805. What a powerful man was this King! His father Guiseppe spoke of the new ideas Napoleon brought to their country. Liberty, Equality, Fraternity. Just words to Giovanni, these words excited much emotion in his father. Other concepts, too, he learned at his father's knee, such as the Code of Napoleon, the written code of administration and judicial conduct. How different from their arbitrary system of justice meted out by the local *despot* (absolute ruler). The closest despot lived in Matera, miles away from their small village. In many ways, his father taught, they still lived in feudal times. The D'Alessandro family clung to their family and their Church. Giovanni would do likewise, for that was the way of his world.

His wife bade the priest goodbye and strolled towards the piazza. Earth tones of brown, whitewashed buildings and black cobblestone paths surrounded them. Angelantonia enjoyed the beautiful weather and felt energetic, so they walked. Giovanni had no immediate chores. Holding Angelantonia's hand, he amused her with his father's story about the Guelphs and Ghibellines. "The Guelphs were a progressive party of leaders long ago. The Ghibellines remained staunch conservatives, loving the old ways, the ways of the nobility. Incessant civil strife resulted in ill will spanning many generations. The gulf between Guelphs and Ghibellines constituted the basis for generations of fighting and civil war. Strife made our village and other cities easy targets for Napoleon."

Party divisions lasted into Giovanni's youth and dominated the social strata of his small village, as well as Matera and Potenza, the two larger villages in the Basilicata area. He added a happy ending. His wife loved the old story.

By the time Giovanni grew into a young adult, Napoleon was only a memory. After his defeat, Austria took over the area of Giovanni's village.

Nothing changed in his daily life. Although the larger, wealthier, more powerful northern cities suffered under Austrian domination, the farmers of the *Mezzogiorno* (southern region) were not considered important enough to fight over. They tended their olive trees and vines of the noble grape known as Aglianico, from which they made their sfuso. Trees and vines made their own life on the rocky, uneven, steep slopes of the countryside.

Contadini walked down the steepest slopes from their village to the fertile ground below, where vegetables and fruits grew in adequate quantities. Goats and cattle produced cheese, milk and meat. Animals roamed freely throughout, but never far away from a villager. Occasionally, Giovanni brought the family *girasoli,* the giant sunflower. He didn't lack for sustenance.

Giovanni looked to the sky. The sun finally burned through the clouds, raising the temperature. He asked Angelantonia if she tired, or needed water. She shook her head. Sitting heavily, she whispered in his ear. "It's time."

Giovanni lost his focus. "Come, I will carry you. We must go home."

Angelantonia smiled. "Wait for the contraction to end. Then I will walk."

Minutes later, he helped her to bed. The midwife arrived, and shooed him out.

"When should I return?"

"I will send notice when the baby arrives."

He wandered to the center of Salandra, shuffling aimlessly. After the excitement, his hunger built, burning in his belly, distracting him from the labor of his pregnant wife. Like most Italians', he lived to eat.

He hung his head in shame, realizing his attention should focus on his wife and her condition while she was so close to labor. His hunger won out. His mother cooked special meals on his birthday. He remembered his mother's cooking like it was yesterday. To be Italian is to love food.

Giovanni sat in the piazza.

Maria and Raphael, their neighbors, waved to him. "Congratulations, Giovanni. May you have a boy."

"Thank you, Raphael. A boy would make my life complete."

"Come, while you wait for the baby I will feed you."

He entered their one story home, furnished with rough-hewn wooden furniture. The wood-burning cook stove stayed warm, ready to bake bread or heat water for pasta at a moment's notice. This dwelling lacked the warmth of his own. He bowed to Raphael and gave a formal greeting. With less guilt and more pleasure he sat down at the table.

Women, what do they talk about? Giovanni smiled and asked, "How long will it take, Maria?"

She served grilled *scamorza* cheese with a little wine. "I don't know. The midwife will call when she is ready."

They chatted about the mass, the sermon of the new, young priest, the weather. Then she brought out pasta prepared by her hand, with the flour, water, eggs and lots of time and loving care. She topped it with *minuich* and *strangulapreuti*, special sauces of her own recipe.

Before dusk the gossiping ended. A woman burst into the home. "Giovanni, Angelantonia's labor is over. Come quickly."

"Thank you, Raphael and Maria."

He ran to his home. Studying his simple wooden structure of several rooms and an outdoor pit, he realized the children needed a separate bedroom. He smiled in the face of more work, knowing he and Angelantonia would have the remaining bed to themselves. With this next child he would clear more land and use the wood to extend the home. How had his father Guiseppe, God rest his soul, ever coped with the demands of a large family?

Giovanni hesitated at the threshold. He hoped for a boy. He said a prayer that his new and growing family live in a time of peace.

Angelantonia smiled at her husband. She held a tiny bundle swaddled in a dark green blanket. "Here is your son, Giovanni. What shall we name him?"

Giovanni cried. A boy! His life was complete. "Let us call him Domenico."

A

CHAPTER THREE

THE RISORGIMENTO

Struggle for Unity in Italy- 1840-1865. The fight for Italian unification changed the lives of peasant farmers.

The D'Alessandro family entered the church in silence.

"Domenico D'Alessandro, your parents Giovanni and Angelantonia wish for you to partake in eternal life. I baptize you in the name of the Father, and of the Son, and of the Holy Spirit. Amen."

The ritual soothed Giovanni and Angelantonia. Candles, the quiet Church and the priest's recitation gave them reason to persevere. The priest handed the infant boy, barely one-week old, back to his mother. Angelantonia immediately put him to breast. She knew this child would need special attention if he were to survive the coming winter. The turning of the fall leaves, her own weakness due to childbirth, and her son's poor suckling heightened her concern. Infant deaths occurred too frequently in Salandra. Change embroiled them during this christening of October twelfth, 1844. Personal changes paled in comparison to the revolution in their village and region.

After prayer, Giovanni and Angelantonia walked outside the church and broke bread with well—wishers and friends gathered about the piazza. As always, social life revolved around the Church. The village worked together, prayed together, and, on the occasion of the birth of a son, celebrated as one.

The women tended to food and children. The men broke into an exclusive group and spoke of farming and politics. Out of earshot of the women, they bragged about their sexual prowess, especially the new fathers. Time flew during their discussions.

Tension tinged with excitement during this period of change. Crops didn't meet expectations for the year. The men complained of erosion and loss of topsoil on their farms. Some speculated it might be related to the rapid clearing of trees, a method used to increase farmland. All agreed, every severe rainstorm held danger. The complaints quickly exhausted, the men turned to politics, the most exciting and enduring topic of conversation.

Political news on this Baptism day revolved around true patriots, freedom fighters, who proselytized the ideals of a centralized Italy. This radical notion stirred the passions of everyone from peasants to patricians. The name of Guiseppe Mazzini came up. Working from exile in France he established *Giovane Italia* (Young Italy) to spread the ideals of nationalism and republicanism. He was not alone.

Giovanni mentioned the neo-Guelph movement. They sought to organize the country around the Pope as both spiritual and temporal leader. Pope Pius IX began an extensive program of reforms in the Papal States, in central Italy surrounding Rome. His ideas spread rapidly to Catholics the world over, through the mechanism of Papal letters.

Radical ideas met stiff resistance in Salandra. Many Contadini spoke of reform. There was little action. But the men of the village of Salandra agreed on one thing. This idea, of unity for their country, would never go away. They agreed to wait and see its form.

*

When Giovanni's newest son Domenico celebrated his fourth birthday in 1848, the men again gathered to share wine and the latest news of the Risorgimento. "Revolutionary change has come to our country," Giovanni said. "The ascendancy of Victor Emmanuel II to King of Sardinia after the abdication of his father Charles Albert has sealed our fate."

His neighbor agreed. "As Charles Albert's defeat by the Austrians stirred our feeling against those conquerors."

Giovanni said, "As his first act in office, Victor Emmanuel retained the tricolor flag, the symbol of a free Italy. This cemented his involvement in the independence movement. The diplomat Conte Camillo Benso Di Cavour came to Sardinia and worked for freedom and unification through diplomatic means."

As Giovanni's boy, the young Domenico held a place at these male gatherings. He listened to his elders but spoke only to the other boys. The adults discussed nationalism. Freedom fighters came from secret societies of southern Italy known as the Carbonari. The village elders realized, even though Domenico did not understand, that France, Germany, England and Spain had already centralized their governments. Since Austria occupied much of the Italian peninsula, some of the men joined with Giovanni in favor of a centralized government, stronger to protect their rights better than the present weak, divided system. Other more conservative farmers spoke for a return to the system of the past. Domenico and his young friends took the principles of liberty, equality and fraternity for granted. His parents still struggled with those radical ideas. They were not sure their lives as farmers would be better with a new government.

Domenico and his young friends seemed to blossom overnight. Domenico listened and learned at these all- male encounters. His life filled with the mundane. He became an expert at tending vines and olive trees. Without comment or complaint, he herded the animals and kept them safe during severe weather, no matter the hour. Rewards were few, food enough, clothing, warmth. But his father allowed him to interact with the other men, and Domenico cherished the encounters. The boy's heart soared when he listened to news of Guiseppe Garibaldi, the most famous freedom fighter in the land and a hero to the common man.

Domenico and his friends played war games in the piazza. "When I grow up, I want to be just like Garibaldi. He travels the world, fighting for us. I'll be his aid."

The other children agreed. "Let's form a squad. We can march and wear uniforms and practice."

Domenico stirred their passions. "We will practice. Soon, Garibaldi will call for us. We will leave the farm and join him. Then he will defeat the Austrians."

Excitement bubbling over, the boys practiced marching for weeks. Domenico realized the possibilities of the world outside Salandra.

News of Garibaldi filtered in to Salandra. While leaving diplomacy to others, Garibaldi organized a force called *The Thousand* to attack and take Rome. That was a short-lived success, as French and Austrians combined to take back their prize city.

Garibaldi never gave up. He led another expedition to aid the Sicilian revolt. The freedom fighters won a tangible victory. This direct and fearsome intervention stirred the hearts of the boys of Salandra. Battles occurred in Sicily, Rome, Sardinia, and other major centers of commerce. Domenico grew and matured with the drumbeat of these revolutionary events.

Salandra and the D'Alessandro family lived as before, a daily struggle to live and survive. In his imagination, Domenico felt different from the others, like one of Garibaldi's soldiers.

*

Domenico D'Alessandro and his father cleared fields to build a bigger home. Other villagers followed suit. One of Domenico's biggest responsibilities became the felling, chopping and stacking of wood for the cooking fire. As the boy grew into a young man, he too noted the loss of soil after heavy rains. But being young and strong, he simply planted more grape vines and olive trees in the washed out areas. These tenacious vines and trees sank deep roots into the rocky soil left over after a storm. In discussions with the other villagers, he hoped this strategy would keep their land productive for the next generation of the family, for in this part of Italy, family was everything.

Besides, they needed more grapes for the wine.

The D'Alessandro family had little enough. They depended on the Church for their spiritual needs, and the extended family for their worldly goods. Most commerce, trade and barter took place first amongst family members, then with the rest of the village and region. Their security came from family and friends in their old villages. His father taught him *Chi gioca solo non perde mai,* the ancient Sicilian phrase. *The man who plays a lone hand never loses.* Contadini required only family and Church. Life was good, if hard. They had their doubts about big government. War was evil for everyone, worst of all for the poor.

Domenico became a man in 1859. With his parent's blessing, he took on the duties and responsibilities of adulthood during the sacrament of Confirmation. The entire country matured with him. His heart quickened along with every other Contadini in Salandra that day in 1859 when Vittorio Emmanuele II read his speech in support of freedom from Austrian rule. Laying down the gauntlet, their King provoked a response. His people rallied around.

The foreign response followed. Austria declared war on the Kingdom of Sardinia. Count Cavour enlisted the aid of the French under Napoleon III, and his coalition defeated the Austrians. Other central Italian regimes were overthrown. A plebiscite voted in favor of annexation to Piedmont in 1860, and unification reached a fever pitch.

Domenico and his family celebrated with the rest of Salandra when the United Kingdom of Italy was proclaimed in Turin, on March seventeenth, 1861. Vittorio Emmanuele II became their first King. The village of Salandra took the day off from labor to celebrate. Peace, they would have. Stronger commerce, and perhaps a better price for their foodstuffs, they hoped would come. An easier life, they prayed. The Contadini watched and waited.

The reality of unification caused difficulties for the D'Alessandro's. Civil war broke out between sections of Italy. The central army battled the Austrians. Salandra became insular. Isolated by strife, months passed without transportation of the farmers' meager goods. The villagers were again forced to rely on their Church and their family. No one from the government came to help the Contadini.

Domenico took this opportunity to exert his independence. As a twenty year-old adult, he wished to expand his lands even further down the slope, into the lush, fertile valley below Salandra. A friend of his, about the same age, struck out and made the long walk to the very bottom of the valley. He planted fruits and vegetables, and that first growing season yielded a bountiful crop. He transported the extra to Taranto, a small fishing village on the Ionian Sea. Upon his return, Domenico's friend became ill with a strange new disease. He suffered rigors and fevers, and became weak and jaundiced. He recovered weeks later, only to relapse again. The priest called this malaria.

Domenico called on God to intervene to help his friend. Frightened by this new and dangerous scourge, he vowed to stay away from the sea and the lowlands where it thrived.

Domenico chose to exert his independence by staying closer to Salandra. He agreed with his father's conservative political ideas. He traveled only part way down the mountain, and enjoyed modest success in his endeavor to plant new crops of fruits and vegetables. The land yielded reasonable amounts and in good years he was able to sell the extra to neighboring regions of Campania to the west, Puglia to the north and Calabria to the south.

Not every villager enjoyed his success. Other neighbors who strayed too low, towards the rivers, had their lands wiped out in the frequent flooding of their waterways during the spring. What other curse, the men asked each other after Mass, could befall their people? What other plague must they endure?

Young men like Domenico prayed, and waited.

*

Powerful forces from across the continent affected the new country of Italy and reached as far south as Salandra. These forces affected commerce and business. Their revolutionary effects equaled those of unification on the social fabric of Italy. In total, these forces changed more for the Contadini than unification. The elders learned the name of the whirlwind in other countries: the Industrial Revolution.

Starting in the early 1810-1820 period in England and Germany, the

Industrial Revolution's spread to southern Europe occurred later, slowed by war, famine and poverty. By the 1870's, the revolution affected southern Europe. Rich urban areas of northern Italy read about new consumer products made by machines, and the powerful and socially adept in the cities craved them. These educated urbanites understood the power of machines and industrialized their cities. In northern Italy, the broad fertile fields yielded better crops to the new, mechanized methods of this bloodless revolution.

For the poor and uneducated and that part of the population knowing only mountain farming like Domenico D'Alessandro, the effects of the Industrial Revolution manifested in different ways, in ways that were not so bloodless.

Taxes bled the farmers. France placed an onerous tax on all Italian wine to keep out competition. The Italian government taxed grain to complete unification and raise funds for a standing army to defeat the Austrians.

Every Italian youth was forced to serve two years in the Italian Army. Worst of all for Domenico, foreign competition brought crop prices down. Continental and even American imports of fruits and vegetables impinged on the local Italian market.

Salandra's economy worsened. Though the D'Alessandro's didn't starve, they lacked variety. The average Contadini suffered a lack of bread. But discretionary spending fell to such low levels it became non-existent. Some less fortunate lost their land and became part of a roving, seasonal work force of laborers. The D'Alessandro's retained their land and avoided catastrophe and bankruptcy.

Basilicata changed as a result of the Industrial Revolution. Emigration increased to the cities, mostly in the north. Urbanization accelerated as landless men sought jobs in factories. These burgeoning cities developed polluted air and water, unable to support the population burden with sub-standard infrastructure. The riches of the cities caused a population boom that offset the problems of famine, disease and natural disaster. Hungry factories demanded natural resources, such as wood, coal, and clean water. Salandra and all of Basilicata suffered more as the revolution progressed. The young and strong North left the old and weak South behind.

*

In 1875, near his birthday, Domenico stood outside the church of Salandra. His formal dress marked the occasion as special. His brothers stood beside, in support. He paced back and forth waiting for the priest to arrive. A smile curled his lips. His mind wandered to the day they met.

In August of 1875, Domenico received a summons from his father.

They walked into the piazza. The boy received a formal introduction to Margharita. After the formal introduction, his parents signed a marriage contract for the children. There was little in the way of dowry.

Neither family had earthly goods, but the parents struggled to follow tradition and do the best possible for their children. Love and survival motivated their actions. Of these, survival was most important. Not only did the bride need to be fertile and strong, and the groom skilled as a provider. They also needed to perform their duties. If the couple's parents could not care for themselves, the children were duty bound to take them in. The couple must reproduce, according to the will of the Church. As Italians, they must experience and enjoy life. Both boy and girl understood these responsibilities.

The families of Salandra interpreted courtship ritual differently. Some elders advocated a radical idea: the children should have a say in the choice of their life partner. Most elders including Domenico's father kept their eyes and ears open, feeling the pulse of young love. Thee Rivelli's felt their daughter would learn to love whoever was chosen. Nothing was needed except obedience. The new couple would learn to love and respect each other with time and experience.

Domenico, age thirty-one and a bachelor, met the young Margharita, age twenty-one and a virgin. They met before the wedding only as a courtesy to the children. Steeped in tradition and obedience, they soon learned they were blessed. Margharita Rivelli found she actually liked the short but strong, happy Domenico D'Alessandro. All knew his farming skills and conservative nature. The men of Salandra held him in high regard. He remained a capable, conservative and outspoken member of their community.

Domenico felt equally blessed. He saw the strong Margharita hauling baskets on her head up the road from the fields in the valley to the heights of Salandra. He was pleased that she possessed a physical beauty, commented on in private conversations with his male friends.

The priest arrived for the ceremony. The sun broke through Salandra's clouds, casting glorious light on the day. Margharita strode down the aisle of Salandra's church on her father's arm. Flowers decorated the pews. A village child spread petals under her feet.

Domenico met her. They held hands, moist with perspiration, in front of the priest. In solemn adherence to ritual the priest intoned, "Do you take this man?"

"Yes. Forever."

"And you take this woman?"

"Yes, in sickness and health."

"In the eyes of God you are married, till death do you part."

They exchanged rings.

The couple reveled in the unique demands of the sacrament. Among all the sacraments, marriage existed since ancient times to bring social order to civilization. They kissed for the first time, each tentative and tender, and walked outside for the celebration. As in the generations before them, the Church led them, guided them, and stayed the center of their social life.

The wedding party started gloriously. The October harvest moon showed on the horizon, and the orange globe of light illuminated their first hours of partying. Home—made food and wines put the entire village into the mood. The weather stayed warm, and dancing broke out. Local musicians with their home—made instruments knew every tune, and generations mixed in delight in the dance.

As the night matured, Domenico and Margharita excused themselves for their honeymoon. Domenico led her to the new wooden cabin he built on his portion of the D'Alessandro property. Small, like his farm, the home was sturdy. The land would support them and all their children, because he wished for many young ones to help him with the farm work and take care of him in his old age. He had no doubts Margharita loved and supported him, because that was her duty and she was obedient. They passed this first night of their marriage without stress and learned to grow together in love and respect.

Their first child, Giovanni Battista D'Alessandro came three years later, in 1878. Margharita and Domenico enjoyed parenthood. Always sharing with family and friends, they sacrificed to feed, clothe and nurse their child. Domenico vowed to clear more land for grazing and farming. He tended the olive trees and the Aglianico grape vines far into the evening. He never complained, for when he returned home, his wife and son waited, smiled for him, and his heart opened. He produced an heir. In Salandra, the family meant everything.

For her part, Margharita worked herding the sheep and cooking meals. Her mother taught these necessities. She made all their clothes, including the baby's. She dressed their son in soft, white cotton breeches and shirt, and had a shoemaker fashion booties out of the softest leather available. After she finished the second pair, she felt satisfied the baby Giovanni would have clothes for a couple of months before he grew too big.

Margharita fabricated beautiful dark brown trousers and a jacket for Domenico for special occasions like Sunday Mass. For underneath she sewed a collarless, soft, white cotton shirt. Try as she might, she couldn't make shoes, so a cobbler made their finest leather into a special pair for her husband. This special outfit distinguished extraordinary occasions.

For work in the fields, she made another soft cotton shirt, sturdier reinforced dark trousers, and a vest with pockets for tools. Leather work boots completed his work attire. From that day, she cleaned and mended his clothes so he would look special, neat and substantial in the eyes of her fellow villagers. As a special treat, she had a wide brimmed fedora fashioned from felt. It fit perfectly. He wore it constantly to protect him from the hot sun in summer and to warm him in winter.

Finally, Margharita thought about herself. There was only one choice for special occasions for women like her. Taking particular care with the cotton, she fashioned the whitest, softest dress, with long sleeves and reaching to the floor in length. Then she added embroidery to the neck, wrists and waist, pulling the waist in slightly to show her figure. She and her mother were very pleased with the result, and she wore it the next Sunday. For everyday clothes, she fashioned a tunic with long sleeves to fit over a separate skirt, also floor length. To aid in carrying heavy loads, she wrapped a long, thin piece of sturdy cotton around her neck, crossing it in front, and then wrapped it tightly around her waist. This functional costume helped her complete the chores and stay comfortably warm in winter, although she didn't use the wrap in summer.

To her great surprise and delight, Domenico bought her a pair of ankle length work boots, specially designed to be easy wearing and comfortable during long walks up and down the hill from Salandra to the fields and markets. Her husband's kindness reminded her to praise both families for arranging this union.

As their love grew, so did the family. Marcello D'Alessandro, their second son, came February 26, 1881, born in their new home in the Piazza Plebriscite.

After the birth, Domenico strode down the path in his warm jacket to see Francis Corananda, Secretary of the Commune, Delegate of the Mayor of Salandra. "I'm here to fulfill my duty, sir, to fill out papers. I have a new son."

Francis Coranada, a respected dignitary, performed his duty with the papers. "Congratulations to you, young Domenico. Let us share a drink of wine in celebration."

Domenico signed his full name as the father.

The official signaled to the witnesses. "Now you men sign."

Neither of his witnesses, Leonardo Leudretti nor Francesco Dagaria the local blacksmith could read or write. "Don't worry. I will sign for you." The secretary signed with a flourish, and it was official. Domenico praised God for their good fortune. Francis Coranada opened a bottle of wine, and they celebrated.

For the rest of the winter, Margharita stayed close to home with the three- year old toddler and the newborn, only cooking, cleaning and mending for those first several months. Domenico laid in a large store of oak from felled trees, working hard so she would not have to wander to find fuel for warmth and cooking.

As winter turned to spring, the parents decided to show their boys to the surrounding neighbors. A favorite annual event, the celebration of *Cavalcata dei Turchi* (Ride of the Turks) fell on the twenty-ninth of May during the Festa San Gerardo. After discussion with friends, Domenico made his decision. They would travel to Potenza and partake of the festivities.

On the appointed day, Margharita rose before the sun to prepare. Excitement forced her up. She'd do anything, anything but sleep. She'd never left Salandra before.

She stoked the cooking fire, started breakfast, and packed food for the journey. Domenico and the children stirred. After an inspection of the sky to gauge the weather, they decided today was a wonderful day. Dressing quickly, the family prayed before breakfast, then left home.

Margharita carried little Marcello on her back, along with the food. Domenico took Giovanni by the hand till he tired, then hoisted him up high above the ground on his shoulders. They progressed quickly, down the long road, further than the children had ever been. As they reached the valley, Margharita sighed. She'd never ventured outside Salandra.

After lunch, their destination in Potenza still lay ten miles distant. Margharita slowed, feet aching. A kindly farmer with a horse drawn cart volunteered to take the children and Margharita in. Domenico jogged beside the cart, speaking with his neighbor and joking with Giovanni.

By sundown, they pulled into Potenza. It was bigger than their expectations. Everywhere people camped and gathered, using their hands and talking to neighbors and new acquaintances. Bonfires proved a magnet for crowds. The atmosphere of the village festival, like the clear night sky above, tingled with excitement.

The family picked out a place to rest and enjoy their food. A little wine finished the meal. They joined in the celebration. After pleasant conversations with their fellow travelers and a little more wine, they slept soundly outdoors on the family blanket, in spite of the revelry all around.

They celebrated the feast day the next morning. During a huge out-door Mass, the family prayed and rejoiced for San Gerardo. They sang Kyrie Eleison, Christi Eleison, Kyrie Eleison and shared Communion with hundreds of other peasants of the Contadini. After the ritual ended, the Church again led the social celebration. Fun broke out. Jugglers, magicians, clowns circulated through the throngs, delighting Giovanni and making fun of his parents. Food, their usual fare as well as variations they had never seen or tasted was available at prices even Domenico could afford.

The wine was not sfuso. Aglianico grape producers from the entire area of Basilicata brought aged, textured wine in wooden casks. Margharita and Domenico couldn't believe how it lingered on the tongue. The bouquet was different from what they made at home. They sampled. They gossiped. Soon, they felt sleepy and took a short nap, except for Domenico. He struck up a conversation with other farmers about their trade.

"Why are the prices so reasonable?" Domenico asked the men.

"The farming economy is poor," his new friends reported. "What last year cost five hundred lire now goes for two hundred fifty. Tend to the farm. Thank God that our farms produce. Next year, you may not be able to buy anything."

The response scared Domenico to his very soul.

Domestic wine prices fell because of French taxation. The domestic textile tax, though, caused clothing prices to escalate. The men grumbled in frustration. Some bought manufactured goods from Milan available in their villages, less expensive than anything local artisans, cobblers, blacksmiths and seamstresses offered. As Domenico rejoined the family, his mind roiled.

Night fell quickly in the high mountains. Because of the feast day, the mood lifted with the darkness. Food and wine vendors entered the piazza. A professional band started serenading. How fine was their music. Old traditional songs and new creations mixed in the air. Domenico asked another women to watch the children. He grabbed Margharita and they twirled around the dancing area, happy as two people can possibly be.

They went back for the boys and took on their neighbor's children. This revelry continued far into the night, dancing, gossip, and utmost satisfaction with life. Not till midnight did the band stop, and another hour passed till it was quiet enough for Margharita to finally sleep.

Giovanni woke up his mother with the first light. She carried Marcello and they walked down the road to a stream to wash and dress properly. After breakfast, they went back for the man of the house. Domenico had a little headache, but was in good enough humor as they returned. Everyone spoke of the Ride of the Turks. Today they'd see the performance. What should they expect?

At ten o'clock, a band of fine horses appeared in the piazza. The riders were of two types: one dressed in foreign clothing to signify the Turks, the others dressed as natives. After introductions, they put on a display of horsemanship and mock battle, twirling and jumping throughout the confines of the town. The children laughed and then cowered at the fierce nature of the battle. Adults clapped and shouted in appreciation of the fine animals and their handlers. After the natives won the skirmish and vanquished the enemy, the festival officially closed.

Margharita and Domenico said tearful good-byes to their new friends. Never before had they experienced such an event. They packed their bags, much lighter now, and began the long walk back to Salandra.

Why couldn't ordinary life be so exciting?

Life returned to normal, with farm work and household chores taking up fifteen hours of the day, and children taking up the rest. Family growth continued. More children brought good luck and a bigger work force. During one of the frequent storms that flooded the lower areas of the valley, the family had another child.

Guiseppe Francesco birthed in 1882. The parents couldn't believe their luck. Three strong boys to help with the farm and care for them in old age. Though the parents never admitted it, times were tough. Each new baby was another mouth to feed, another responsibility. They understood the reality of farming in Salandra. Domenico and Margharita worked hard but barely scraped by.

When their first girl, Mariangela, was born in 1889, they thanked God that Giovanni was old enough to work the farm like an adult.

The D'Alessandro's could no longer buy outside goods. The collapse of produce prices left them with no spendable income. They bartered for everything they couldn't grow on the farm. Domenico did allow one trip outside Salandra a year, either to Matera for the Festa Della Bruna, or back to Potenza for the August fifteenth Sagra di San Rocco feast. Alas, they had no money to spend. They enjoyed the ambiance anyway. As the dancing and singing continued with other Contadini in the same straits, they praised God and delighted in the beauty of nature.

The adults could see the trend. Subsistence became harder. Life became much more struggle than fun and festivals.

The D'Alessandro family suffered a communal shock with the arrival of their second girl. Her parents anticipated great joy. The midwife clucked and shook her head while attending the labor. Margharita demanded an explanation.

The midwife brought the child to her breast, and pointed to the left hand. It was horribly deformed. Not only that, but the left. More superstitious midwives believed this left- hand deformity signified a mark of the Devil. Margharita would have nothing of it. Taking her baby girl Antonia, she stared fiercely at Domenico. He kissed the baby and his wife, and pledged his love for both.

They raised her as normally as possible. There were certain realities that both parents understood. Antonia would not marry. They could never arrange a suitable union with her deformity. She would be their responsibility forever, another mouth, crippled, and a spinster.

The family suffered a great loss.

*

The older children, Marcello and Giovanni, learned they were not allowed to tease or other-wise harass their sister. Domenico sat them down when Giovanni turned thirteen and told them their duty. They would protect Antonia from ridicule. They would treat her normally, and she would be given certain responsibilities as a member of their house. She was family, and in Salandra, in the D'Alessandro home, family was sacred.

There would be no more children. There were too many mouths to feed, too little time in the day to make the farm produce.

All their friends, all their relatives had large families. Neighboring villages burst to overflowing. Men moved down the slopes and built more homes. As farms divided after the death of a husband and father, more trees were cut to expand the fields. Storm runoff washed away the topsoil, and what was left produced little useful crop. Mosquitoes bred in newly formed swamps. Diseases called malaria and cholera wiped out some of the enlarging population of Salandra and environs in Basilicata Province. That year alone, a cholera epidemic killed fifty-five thousand peasants.

Despite famine and plague in the countryside, the cities grew. Italy's population exploded, and with it came hungry mouths to feed. Now, the D'Alessandro's all knew the truth.

They knew they were poor.

A

CHAPTER FOUR

IN WITH THE NEW

1890 in Salandra. In famine and economic collapse, the whims of youth take on added importance, unraveling family structure.

Their parents couldn't separate the brothers Giovanni and Marcello. Giovanni Battista D'Alessandro, the eldest, remained slender and carried an erect, military bearing. His lean face and closely cropped brown hair fit the military mold. A scrawny moustache showed his vanity. He seldom smiled and looked upon the world as a straightforward challenge. Being the eldest, he held a privileged place in the family. His vocation as a farmer was pre-ordained by his father.

Strong and bulkier than his older brother, Marcello was quick to smile, and equally quick to fight if he felt wronged. A little of the devil lived on in his pranks. As the second son, he'd have a smaller portion of the farm.

Their short stature and prominent noses marked them of the same family. They remained inseparable because of their living conditions. Their home burst at the seams with children, all sleeping in the same bed. The boys grew strong together, learning side by side about the seasons, which clouds signified rain, how to plant vegetable seeds for the best yield. Intelligent and strong, the boys grasped the essentials of farming quickly. They quizzed each other on reading and writing. Those skills were unusual in Salandra.

Domenico used the boys to help on the farm, one day asking the boys to drag the wood he had cut, the next having them clear rocks from a new field. His greatest pride grew from the accomplishment that his boys, above all the other male children of the village, could read and write. So their father gave them a little time after the chores and before dinner as play time. That is when the brother's bond flourished.

They were friends, collaborating on typical boyhood endeavors like swimming in the river to cool the hot summer days. They played *football*, they dared each other with tests of bravery while climbing a tree or crossing a stream. Sharing secrets learned from the adult's conversations, they whispered in private about that bigger world outside the family. They mimicked adult conversations.

"I'll have the biggest family, because I'm the strongest," Giovanni said.

"Didn't you hear the padrone speak? I'll astound you with my stories of travel and riches," Marcello replied.

Giovanni stomped around the farm, incredulous. "You would leave home?"

"Of course. I can do anything I set my mind to."

Such a thing was unheard of in Salandra. Where else would a family man live?

In the early 1890's, the *padrone* system of contract labor took hold in Italy and Greece. A padroni was a bilingual man who enlisted unskilled laborers in Italy for work in the USA.

The padroni offered to pay steamship costs, food, and expenses. The attraction of a guaranteed job in America, and earning enough to send money back home attracted younger men, especially those other than the eldest. Many single, strong but dreadfully poor southern Italians signed. They looked to America to build their fortune, since wages and opportunities abounded. The Contadini had dreams of saving money, helping their families and loved ones back home, and escaping the poverty and disease of Italy. They planned to return to Italy. That was their hope.

Living conditions deteriorated in Basilicata. An Italian from another family wrote a letter to a friend in the United States: *"Things go badly here. Many Contadini here do not eat bread. They live on potatoes and beans. One can only find work three or four months of the year. Why do so many go to America? Because they are better off there. When someone returns from America to tell us that there are fewer discomforts, many of the men cannot resist the temptation to go and find out for themselves."* (1)

The brothers listened respectfully and retired to the farm to speculate. Being the eldest, Giovanni knew he could work the land and continue to make a living. The D'Alessandro's owned their land, a step up from the itinerant peasants Giovanni noted roaming the countryside, looking for work throughout the year. The peasants had no place to call home.

Marcello learned he'd have to take care of himself. His portion would be smaller and less likely to sustain a family. From the beginning, he looked outward for opportunity. Another trait distinguished Marcello from the rest of his family and village.

He dreamed.

Always willing to gamble and take a chance, he consistently beat Giovanni in their childhood games. Though he sometimes got injured from trying too hard, he recovered and learned from his mistakes. He did more than listen to the letters from America, to the padrone, and to visitors who had been there.

He believed.

He dreamt of a better life, with gold paved streets of America providing work at high wages. He believed in riches. How nice it would be to own land and let other peasants work it for him in America. Fruit and vegetables from America arriving for sale in Potenza and Matera looked healthier and tasted better than the produce from his father's farm. Why couldn't he have it all, riches, wealth, a new and easier way of life?

Marcello shared his plan with Giovanni. "The day after Confirmation, when our Church proclaims I am a man, I will leave Salandra and go to America. Tell no one, Giovanni. It is our secret."

Giovanni could not condone the heartache such a plan would cause in their parents. "Why, brother? We have everything here we could possibly need. The sun and it's warmth causes the seedling to sprout. I feel satisfied when the crop grows after all our hard work. We never lack for food. When I see the church campanile, I am proud of Salandra and the farm. It's been this way for centuries. Why aren't you content?"

Marcello didn't want to disappoint his family, for in Salandra, the family is everything. Still he was not content. His father and brother still believed the *patria* (native land) extended only as far as the sound of the local bell tower. The families in the village knew this as *campanillismo*.

Marcello couched his plan in terms of a temporary arrangement, leaving the door open for a return. He didn't want to lie. "I don't have what I want. I hear the padrone speak of America. Everything about it sounds exciting. There is more to the world than farming this old soil. I want to find what's out there. Do you know I've never even been to Rome? They say there are Roman ruins almost 2,000 years old."

"It's true. The priest tells us that."

"Brother, you will keep this secret?"

Giovanni stomped and scratched his moustache. "Where will you get the money? How will you move about, what will you do? What of our family heritage?"

"You have the farm. You will care for our parents when they are old."

"You will hurt our parents deeply. Marcello, I don't agree, but because we are brothers, I will keep your secret."

Marcello's plans changed in puberty. At age thirteen, he never guessed at the influence of the opposite sex. He learned new life lessons.

The lessons started in earnest when his mother enlisted Marcello as a soldier in the Army of Christ. All sacraments demanded serious commitment, Confirmation more than others. The rank of soldier was not conferred lightly or to anyone, like Baptism. Adults, those studying and understanding the basis for their religion, received Confirmation. The Catechism; the New Testament; the Apostle's Creed. These works, as well as ideas and local lore of the priest, required study and contemplation prior to consideration of Confirmation.

Being literate helped Marcello in the preparation. He stood out from the crowd of children in this respect. The priest instructed Marcello and other children by reading the relevant works to them. Marcello soon took over reading the texts to the other children. Domenico and Margharita were proud when the priest praised their son's diligence, memory and reading ability. It was so unusual in their village. Soon, the priest visited the family home. "Marcello is ready for Confirmation, if that is your wish."

Domenico thrust out his chest. "Yes, padre. He has studied many hours."

"I will summon him for the test."

The priest summoned Marcello to the Church. He sat, alone, with only God and the priest watching. The priest recited a question and the boy, sitting in front of him on the rough wooden bench, recited the answer. "Who is God?" and "What is the Trinity?"

Finally, the ultimate question. "Marcello, if your life and your freedom depended on it, would you denounce your God and your religion?"

Marcello thought, struggled and sweat. He hadn't pondered these questions. Keeping cool and collected, he prayed and meditated and only then answered. "God is the supreme being, who made us all."

Hours later, the priest took him by the hand and walked outside to Domenico and Margharita. "Marcello has learned well. He passed."

Marcello and the family breathed a sigh of relief.

"The next time the Bishop comes to Salandra, Marcello will be Confirmed."

As the bishop owned much of the surrounding land and rented to many farmers of Salandra, his presence made everyone nervous. The holy sacrament of Confirmation made the Bishop happy. The villagers relaxed during the yearly ritual of Confirmation.

As his father Domenico relaxed, Marcello sat in the piazza studying for the Bishop's visit. His mind wandered, and at this stage of development it focused on few things. He noticed a girl his age, a pretty girl, who returned his furtive glances. "What is your name?"

"Donata Onorato," she giggled, and returned to her study. "Mama says I'm not to talk to you.

He hadn't contacted her before. Their families were of different social beliefs. This went back to the conflicts of the Guelphs and Ghibellines. The feud continued during unification, with one family on the side of the Freedom Fighters, the other aligned with the northern Italian nobility. Domenico told Marcello the D'Alessandro's felt the Onorato's took on airs and acted as if they were better than other families in the village.

Marcello didn't believe in feuds. His stirring and unsettling attraction to this girl in his class caused him to speak. "My name is Marcello. Do you want me to read the lesson to you?"

"Yes, please. I can't figure out the words." She smiled her best and brightest smile. They studied the lesson till it was time to go home.

He saw her many times before the bishop arrived. On Confirmation day the village adults turned out, gossiping and vying to kiss the Bishop's ring as he entered the church. Other children worried about questions they might receive from the Bishop. Marcello focused on Donata. The attraction grew strong. Should he approach her?

His father said no.

What could he ask her without seeming foolish?

"How are you today?"

What if she ignored him?

He'd never live down such a snub.

What if she answered?

He'd shared these weighty questions with his brother and friend Giovanni.

Although a good listener, his older brother wasn't much help. He had no special attraction to girls. "When the time comes, Domenico will arrange a suitable union."

"Giovanni, you are boring. You think only of farming." Even so, Marcello bounced his fears and anxieties off his Sphinx like brother, and defeated his demons.

The children filed into the church, on their best behavior. The Bishop anointed them with oils and slapped their cheeks, making them soldiers in the Army of Christ.

After wards, the village gathered for a celebration. Marcello steeled his nerves and struck up a conversation. There was a quiver in the voice. "Hello, Donata. What a glorious day to be Confirmed in the Church. How are you?"

"Hello, Marcello." She smiled and curtsied. "I am very happy."

Her mother Rosantonia Onorato saw the interaction and took immediate steps to circumvent the damage. She grabbed Donata by the hand. "Our family does not speak with the likes of the D'Alessandros."

Rosantonia screeched at her daughter. After a piercing look of the evil eye to Marcello, she took Donata's hand and left the festivities.

The campanile rang its song. Marcello heard only discordant notes. Heart heavy, embarrassed, Marcello's vision of campanillismo changed. He remembered his boyhood promise to Giovanni. He had no unbreakable bonds to his country. He could break the old taboos. He could have whatever he wanted, whatever he set his young mind to.

Why not follow his spirit?

—

As time passed, Marcello began to look on his interaction with Donata in a more favorable light. Her parents didn't have to know of their meetings. Not only was he a confirmed soldier, he had a love. He replayed the encounter over in his head. After the fifth time his brother would no longer listen.

At the celebration of Marcello's fourteenth birthday, at the special dinner in his honor, he dared ask his mother about the conflict between the families. In their simple home in the Piazza Prebricite in Salandra, mother and son looked furtively for a place to chat. "Domenico, we need more wood."

Domenico walked outside with Giovanni.

Mother and son seized a moment's privacy for a discussion. Margharita understood, since it only became her family's feud through marriage. "I'll try to explain, my son. It is the prerogative of parents to expect you will follow through your life all curses, taboos and customs. That is the way of the village. It's been that way for many generations."

"Is there no cure for these beliefs?"

"Sometimes when a person acts with great discretion, deviation is allowed. Think about that, Marcello. Act carefully. Perhaps your father Domenico won't forbid it if you use caution and tact. I'll try to speak of the matter on your behalf."

Marcello kept up the subterfuge, seeing Donata around Salandra, and more often in the fields below. He ached for the days when they met. A quick hello and they relayed important news that couldn't wait. Sometimes they found time for a more leisurely recitation of events since their last clandestine report. After a few minutes it was over, although in Marcello's heart her voice spoke endlessly. He dreamt of her beauty. He was sure she felt exactly the same way. The only trouble was, he wasn't sure what his feelings meant to either of them. Their future existed in the next minute, the next encounter. Marcello's dreams of life outside Salandra faded away.

—

On his seventeenth birthday, Marcello and Domenico walked the farm. His father picked an area of the farm with a view and privacy. Surrounded by crops, grape-vines and sheep, the men sat in the shade of an olive tree. The sun shone on huge, puffy white clouds. A cool fall breeze blew. The leaves turned bright, vibrant colors of red and orange. About the same height, Marcello's muscular build approached the strength and girth of Domenico. His father brought up the rules of life for the Contadini in Salandra. This wasn't about the birds and the bees. Business and life decisions guaranteed survival. The D'Alessandro family must survive. "Son, its time you understood the customs of our family. I will choose a wife for you soon, as I did for your brother Giovanni. You will inherit a portion of our farm. You are old enough to make your own life and have a family. It's the way of our village, our country. You will join society as an adult. You'll find everyone in the village helps everyone else."

Marcello listened respectfully as his father reviewed how the farm would pass on after his death, how the three boys would each receive a third of the land they struggled to cultivate. The headstrong Marcello wanted to shout out his belief that the farm failed, that soon it would not grow enough for the family. He held his tongue. His father mentioned marriage arrangements he contemplated. At the age of eighteen, he would arrange the union that would spawn Marcello's family.

Like an animal in a cage, Marcello paced. Anger raged inside his head, in his belly, his loins. He had to speak out. He had to make his wishes, his feelings known to his father. It was not too late. "Father, excuse me. I know someone. Perhaps you could approach Donata Onorato."

Domenico hushed him. "No, you do not choose. No, you will not wed any Onorato. We will not speak of it again. There is a feud. Because we own our land, because we are Guelph, they don't mix with us. They would never accept my overture. Do you not understand?"

After their discussion, Marcello withdrew to the piazza. His father's attitude stole his life force. He didn't know what to do. For the previous months, mind, body and spirit filled with Donata, he felt bliss.

He paused as the campanile rang. Strange sounds, coming from *their patria*. Sounds of despair, defeat. Marcello remembered his boyhood vow to see Rome, to see the America. Was the world insane? Was no one listening?

At his next meeting with Donata he understood the reason for his father's talk. The Onorato's, Rocco and Rosantonia, had a similar talk with their daughter. She tried to make her wishes known. It was too late. Such a tear in the social fabric was not condoned. Her parents already had a match, a contract on their word of honor. She would marry Pasquale Albano, a local farmer of Salandra. Her parents thought this match very suitable. First, the families liked and respected each other. Second, Pasquale had come from a more similar farming background. They might not be as prosperous, but they would be happy. Pasquale was the eldest, entitled to more farmland than Marcello. It was done. No discussion. No question.

Summer heat turned to moderate days of fall. The relationship cooled between Marcello and Donata. It wasn't easy, but everyone in the village conspired to keep them apart. Young heats broke quickly, but mended slowly.

Wedding preparations continued. The ceremony, though beautiful, brought melancholy to the D'Alessandro's, the Albano's and the Onorato's. What was ordinarily a festive occasion became quiet, subdued. The villagers rued a celebration spoiled by despair. Their superstitions foretold disaster.

On September tenth 1898 Donata Onorato became the wife of Pasquale Albano in the Catholic Church of Salandra.

Marcello D'Alessandro determined the day of Donata's wedding to follow his instincts and set a new course in life. He needed to break away and breathe again. He could no longer live in such a stifling environment. He thought it through on his own. Old rules needed to give way to the new. He shared his plan with Giovanni. He would leave this stifling atmosphere in Salandra. He would go to America!

The fire of love burned longer in Donata. She remained friendly with

Marcello throughout her pregnancy. On August sixteenth 1899 she gave birth to a son. They named him Rocco. She and Pasquale discussed the bleak economy of their village and the prospects for their son. Donata mentioned Marcello, a man who owned land and was better off than most. Pasquale grudgingly consented. They asked Marcello to be godfather.

Accepting the title of godfather mandated responsibilities in their village and their Church. A godfather's duty authorized supervision to insure his godson grew in the knowledge of God. If the parents were unable to care for the child, they expected the godfather to raise the child as his own. The special relationship between godfather and son remained sacred through the generations. Marcello swore to keep it so. He consented to the chore. With good intentions, he visited the boy often and doted on his every need.

Pasquale Albano did not like the visits from Marcello. His home life grew discontented. He spent time with other women. On Roccos' first birthday, in the midst of the celebration, he fought with Donata. They argued. She didn't know how to please Pasquale. As she replied to his incessant questioning, he hit her. Again. Again!

As the gossip made its way to the D'Alessandro farm, Marcello grew angry. He'd go to America, where people made their own choices.

When the Polizia came the next week to gather recruits for the army, Marcello acted. He couldn't wait two years in the army before living his dream. He left Salandra. He'd not risk jail for avoiding military service.

He planned never to return.

A

CHAPTER FIVE

EMIGRATION TO OPPORTUNITY
Italy-France- 1900, 1901

Over one hundred years ago, Italians did not act in a vacuum. The stories of Marcello's countrymen were well known throughout Italy, spread by padrone and worker alike. His country sent over three hundred thousand mostly single male Contadini from the Mezzogiorno to America between 1881 and 1890. The New Wave of Immigration began. Marcello saw young men his age leaving in droves.

The numbers rose from 19891 to 1900. The Italian population had doubled since unification and the Industrial Revolution. What made men such as Marcello leave?

For most in the Mezzogiorno, farming failure mandated a change. They called it *miseria*—misery. An Italian immigrant wrote: *"For breakfast we had polenta, then held on from noon until one or even two in the afternoon and had more polenta, and polenta again in the evening, or perhaps bigoloto (a kind of pasta), sometimes with some greens braised in vinegar or sautéed in a drop of oil. This except Thursday, when my mother would go down to Brenna to buy rice from the miller and make soup with a few beans or some greens, and then we'd feel as if we were putting on weight with every spoonful. But this only happened on Thursdays. There was no bread, because we only had it once or twice during the harvest when we'd go out into the fields, women and children combing the furrows like mice to gather stray grains of wheat, grind them, and made loaves to satisfy a hunger as old as time."* (2)

Man does not live by bread alone, but when there is not even bread?

Because of deforestation, what little arable land existed in the mountainous regions washed away. The D'Alessandro's and the Albano's experienced erosion on their property. Erosion cause the upland farms to fail. The runoff choked rivers and streams of the lowlands, turning them into swamps unsuitable for agriculture, but perfect for mosquitoes. Thousands died from cholera and malaria.

Many starved. The rest stayed hungry, no help in sight. No social programs except prayer. No strong central government to relocate the poor and disadvantaged. The government, tied up in war, continued to fight the Austrians. Northern Italy fought against the South.

Politics changed little for the Mezzogiorno. Unification of Italy did not end suffering. Unification brought high taxes on grain and government corruption. These were not new, only unexpected after the fine rhetoric of the revolution. The Contadini were sick of war, yet the southern sections in the Mezzogiorno revolted against the abuses of the centralized government, such as the rising price of salt. After the northern forces crushed the revolt, poverty and resentment grew. For these reasons, those in Salandra steered clear of politics.

They avoided everything political except the draft.

The central government had modern ideas about unification. The Army draft became one of their tools for unification. National law mandated all citizens serve two years between age eighteen and forty. To promote unity, northern residents were sent south to learn the dialects and customs. These upper class, educated youngsters dismissed Army service as a vacation.

The southerners, uneducated, poor, family oriented, felt out of place so far from their campanile. Many refused to serve after harsh treatment and discrimination at the hands of northern officers and populace of the urban north. Draft dodgers faced capture and imprisonment. Rather than face disgrace, many emigrated. Most villagers in the small farming communities like Salandra had no loyalty to a united Italy. They saw no reason to suffer the consequences of disobedience. They left for a better life in the New World.

For those without land, the job market improved in large industrialized cities like Milano. However, the cost of living rose precipitously, doubling from 1870 to 1890. The vicious cycle spiraled down. There seemed to be no way out of poverty for the masses in Italy. The elders might accept their fate, but younger, unmarried men did not. They saw opportunities for a better life here and now on Earth. Perhaps they didn't believe the Church's teaching that their eternal reward awaited in Heaven.

In the 1890's in Salandra, their God seemed to desert them. Earthquakes hit Mount Vesuvius and areas of Basilicata. To add insult to injury, that most Italian of symbols, drinking wine, suffered a threat close to extinction. Phylloxera, a disease of the roots of grape vines, nearly wiped out the vineyards of southern Italy. In Italy, *a meal without wine is like a day without the sun.* Young Italians had enough. They acted. They emigrated in droves.

Marcello would go to America. He planned this trip as an individual. He had personal reasons. But he was not alone. Everywhere he turned, other Southern Italians struggled to America to be free.

He would forget Donata and start a new life. In America, he heard people lived unbound. They made their own choices, without interfering parents dictating everything: wife, job, even religion. Americans made a comfortable wage, and some became fabulously wealthy. The *ritornati* (returning Italian immigrants) told him the truth. So did the padrone.

That was his dream. He told no one, not even Giovanni, the true reason for leaving Salandra. Deep in his heart of hearts, Marcello felt anger, bitterness and frustration. These emotions festered in his soul.

Betrayal.

His parents betrayed him. They favored Giovanni with the best land. What was wrong with him?

He loved a girl and was told it couldn't be. Why wasn't he good enough to have Donata? With all the hardship of this earthly life, wasn't he due a little love?

He deserved more. Surely, he knew of Earthly rewards. It couldn't be as the Church preached, that our only reward is not of this life, but is Heaven. Marcello kept the passions and the doubts locked inside. To others in the village, he took the loss of love and family gracefully and moved on with his life.

He was better than the others.

Marcello had another burning desire. Emigrating to America was his dream, the ultimate adventure. This trip would satisfy his wanderlust, growing inside him like a cancer. This new experience would separate him from other farmers and landowners of the village. Perhaps his bold decision might convince his father and his Donata of his worth as a man.

The night before leaving, Marcello had requested a private meeting with his father. They met in the center of the piazza in Salandra. Warm sunshine, whitewashed walls, and heated tempers. As an eighteen-year-old Confirmed adult, he had that right to speak man to man with his father. Domenico remained strong, though showing signs of age, with graying hair and a droop of his dark facial skin. His arms could lash out at any time and sent the young man tumbling across the piazza.

Marcello made a statement. "I will leave Salandra for America. I won't be a burden to my family. As my last request, father, consider giving my portion of the farm to Antonia. As the youngest sister she needs the means to sustain herself."

Domenico sat silently, bowled over by this headstrong child. Such insolence from his own son. And this unheard of request, to give land to a female! Marcello was a good son. He had his young heart broken during the scandal with the Onorato girl. How to respond?

Domenico spoke slowly, respectfully, as though to a fellow villager. "My son, I understand your feelings. They are real and painful. But, in Salandra, in our family, things are done as our ancestors arranged for us so many years ago. You cannot have my blessing to leave for America. You must stay here and do your duty to your mother and me. You must not leave. You have duties and responsibilities here. Most of all, you have a family that loves you, and in our country, in our culture, family is everything."

Marcello stood and faced his father. His last appeal failed. He felt good about his intentions, but he was not disappointed. "This is goodbye, father. I cannot stay in a place such as this. I will see another world. I will not be back."

He walked out of their meeting and calculated. With his limited resources, he made a rational, stepwise plan. Thinking with clarity never before experienced, he returned to his home on the Piazza Prebricite and said goodbye to each of his siblings. Then he approached his mother. She jumped up, kissing him and begging him not to leave. She cried, fell to his feet and prayed to God to change his mind. He allowed her to vent her feelings, kissed her, and went to bed. He'd visit France by train. From there he'd make his way across the ocean.

Marcello left Salandra the next morning.

Surprises arrived by the minute. From the mountainous terrain of Salandra, through dry low hills near Napoli, he traveled on foot and cart. Trains took him to the flat but productive plains of northern Italy. Booking the international train in Milan, he traveled north through Italy into France. The cold as they crossed the Alps into France came as yet another surprise.

What a change of scenery!

For the next months he worked, learning French and saving money. Starting as a laborer, he moved up to dishwasher and finally cook, relying on skills learned from his mother in the kitchen. Facile with language, he picked up a local accent quickly. As soon as he had the fare, Marcello made up his mind.

I'll go to America.

Now.

Boulogne-Sur-Mer, on the northern coast of France, near England across the Channel was the closest port. The Holland-America Line plied a regular route from Rotterdam, Boulogne-Sur-Mer, then direct to New York. He paid half fare, with the promise to work in the ship's galley. He met several other Italians and they decided to travel together. Rocco, Mario and Francesco invited Marcello to celebrate their last night in the Old World on December 18, 1901.

The cafe barely contained their excitement. In the low lighting, they smoked and drank French wine. The Fleur-de-lys became their proximate symbol of freedom.

"I look ahead with the greatest anticipation," Francesco announced. "The New World, it promises me a better life."

Marcello didn't mention his aborted love life or his family. He tried to forget the military draft. He looked only to the future. "It's all I've dreamed about."

They celebrated into the night. Tomorrow promised excitement. They would sail on the *T.S.S. Rotterdam III* to America. He and his friends celebrated the birth of new experience, freedom and success.

After a satisfying breakfast provided by the shipping line, Marcello walked into the huge barracks housing the Holland America offices. He and his fellows were stripped, their baggage fumigated, and given a thorough medical examination.

"Why must we submit to an examination?"

To his complaint, the official of the Holland America Line said, "If you don't make it through immigration in New York, the Holland America line will have to pay the cost of transport back to France. America only takes healthy immigrants."

Marcello owned two suits, and wore both of them. As he stripped, his friends Francesco, Rocco and Mario and the medical officials made a joke at his expense. Marcello's dander rose. "Is this how you treat your customers?"

"We just follow orders, designated by America. Otherwise you will be sent back here at our expense.."

There were no further complaints or questions from the pilgrims. They were ushered outside, to an area fenced off from the rest of the dock. They passed this first test of their journey.

The ship would soon leave Europe and his old life.

Marcello saw the sea spray in the air, so different from Salandra. He smelled the ocean and the fish, foreign to his experience. He examined the other passengers, noting the different groups boarding. Several families of husband, wife and children huddled. Parents spent their time hushing excited children. Many young, singly or in groups, waited with them in the holding area. Everyone, man, woman and child, had a bundle or sack to contain their worldly possessions. One woman carried hers in a small basket, balanced on top of her head. The others, striving for a modern look, carried valises or satchels. Their relatives waited and yelled to them from outside the fence. No one paid any attention to see off the four young men.

To Marcello, the travelers appeared to be similar in good health, poor economic status, and excitement. He saw the rich people take a special boat out to the ship and enter the upper levels. First Class passengers, the sailor said. They seemed happy, and the crew treated them courteously.

The four young men, emigrants booked in steerage, passed time on the dock till a rowboat arrived. First and second-class fares paid more. Steerage passengers waited till last and received minimal amenities. Herding ten passengers on the boat, the French officials said goodbye and pointed to the fine steamship with the single yellow stack, the *Rotterdam III*.

All heads turned to admire their transportation to America. No one had ever seen such a ship. Marcello asked the sailor about the ship.

"You are very lucky," the man replied in French. "She is the strongest and fastest transatlantic steamship. Capable of fourteen knots, the ship measures four hundred eighty five feet in length. You will have a gentle voyage. She is propelled by twin screws for stability, a new design. She displaces eight thousand one hundred eighty six tons."

Marcello rubbed his head. "I don't understand. Is that good?"

"The *Rotterdam III* is one of the largest vessels plying the North Atlantic. That is very good."

As the sailor rowed slowly out into the harbor, the ten young men saw the *Rotterdam's* bulk. The magnitude of their trip, crossing thousands of miles of the North Atlantic in late December, both inspired and intimidated. "My friends," Marcello said, "If we can do this, we can do anything, including conquer America!"

The friendly sailor motioned for them to walk up the ladder to the ship.

Marcello led, followed by his new best friends Rocco, Francesco and Mario. The sailor showed them to their room, one room for ten men.

They were used to cramped conditions at home and did not complain. Docile, the men settled in on the bunks and the floor and traded their life stories. Francesco knew a little English. As soon as his knowledge of English leaked out, he was inundated with questions, and became the acknowledged leader about anything and everything American. Everyone wanted to learn as much of English and America as they could during the voyage.

At eight AM sharp, on the crest of the high tide, the *Rotterdam* blew its steam whistle. The men ran upstairs to view the departure. Marcello got a place beside the rail, just in time to gaze over Boulogne-Sur-Mer from the water. What an amazing site! Deep blue water turned to azure at the junction of the rocky coast with the sea. Hectares of the city in the distance, faded imperceptibly into farmland, which gradually faded into barren, brown hills.

Heart beating rapidly, chest heaving, he looked in awe over the biggest city in his small world. He wondered at how small it became minutes later, as the *Rotterdam* left the port and picked up speed, heading southwest towards the North Atlantic to America. How big would New York be in comparison?

As the harbor at Boulogne-Sur-Mer in northern France withdrew, leaving only the basic elements of water, air and sky, he watched the horizon expand for a thousand miles. He pondered this decision. Marcello sat on deck, watching his native continent slowly fade from sight. "Did I do the right thing?"

One thing was certain. He would succeed, or he would die trying. There was no turning back.

Marcello smiled, sun warming his face on the deck of the ship. Looking back on the fading landscape of France, Marcello reflected on his family's betrayal. He vowed to be stronger, not so vulnerable. In America things would be different. Gold paved streets, good wages, jobs…and perhaps wealth. Goodbye, father. Goodbye, Old World.

Hello to the New World.

A

CHAPTER SIX

Isle of Hope, Isle of Tears
ELLIS ISLAND, 1902

The immigrants braved a winter passage to face the unknown and unfamiliar metropolis that was turn of the century New York City.

The *Rotterdam III*, its distinctive yellow smokestack belching coal laced black steam, passed the southern tip of England and headed west. Sea breeze, the rolling waves, strange languages brought challenges with every moment. Marcello struck up a conversation with Francesco. Mario and Rocco milled about. They all wished to listen, hear English words, and learn what was to come.

But today Francesco was all out of English. "My uncle has made the passage many times. He spoke of a storm with incredibly tall waves, howling wind, and seasickness to die for."

"But he made it to New York, yes?"

Francesco nodded. "After the storm, my uncle warned me about his worst fear: Ellis Island. They have another test, a medical test more difficult than the one in Boulogne-Sur-Mer. My uncle said, *'You know what? When you get over to Ellis Island they're going to be examining your eyes with a hook. Don't let them do it because you know what? They did it to me—and one eye fell in my pocket.'"* (3)

Marcello and his friends laughed. "Francesco, it couldn't be so. You made it up!"

Francesco disagreed. "What uncle said is true. You will see in a few days."

They spoke of their dreams. The men all wished for riches and an easier life, where they had the right to chose for themselves. They cut all ties to the old world.

Each night before bedtime, Marcello remembered the examination and trembled. He could not suffer the indignity of a forced return to Europe. America was his destiny, his future. His escape from his family's betrayal. He must pass the test.

What if he should fail?

Passing into the Atlantic from the Channel, all aboard noticed the rougher, darker water. The passage into open ocean meant changes for those below decks. Steerage passengers including Rocco became ill with seasickness and took to their beds for the rest of the trip.

Marcello noticed shorter lines at the kitchen during mealtime, although that didn't translate into bigger portions. The seas didn't make him a bit uncomfortable. He kept up his cooking duties at every meal, and since fewer passengers came to eat, he helped himself to even bigger portions. He must keep up his strength. Rocco stopped eating for two days due to nausea. He recovered, however, and the small group of friends resumed eating their meals together. They looked forward to the excitement ahead.

One particularly windy day, the friendly French sailor delivered a case of yellow fruit to steerage. Looking for a little fun, the sailor demonstrated how they should eat, in great detail and with many hand motions. "Ba-na-na. Eat. Very good."

Marcello thanked the sailor for his courtesy. As instructed, he ate the outside yellow part and threw away the rest, but didn't like it much. It left him with an upset stomach. The sailor, doubled over with laughter, sympathized but couldn't help. Marcello remembered the word to add to his growing English vocabulary.

No one could tell the men exactly how long the trip might last. Mario thought the journey was of three thousand miles, but didn't know how long that would take. Francesco said his uncle mentioned one to two weeks on board, but none of them believed the trip could vary so much. The *Rotterdam III*, so huge and powerful, would speed across the waves no matter the weather. To settle the question, Marcello instructed Francesco to ask a crew- member. During the crew inspection of the steerage area, he did so. Between Italian,

English and Dutch, Francesco learned the trip took between seven and fourteen days. Their research did little to settle the question.

The mild mid-winter weather held without major storms. After three days, the *Rotterdam III* approached the frigid regions of the North Atlantic known for icebergs. Out of wireless contact with Europe and America, without sophisticated navigational capabilities, the captain was forced to rely on visual cues. At night, a bright moon sufficed to avoid collisions. A minor storm clouded the sky. They experienced no problems, though Marcello worried about accidents.

That night, with visibility limited, the captain ordered all stop to avoid any possibility of collision with an iceberg. Everyone aboard understood the danger. Engines idling, the ship took on an exaggerated roll from wave action. More steerage passengers suffered seasickness. Every stray sound might be an approaching iceberg. Marcello and his friends couldn't sleep.

By the grace of God, the next morning showed clearing skies and fewer clouds. The *Rotterdam* continued on at full speed. Mario and Rocco walked the deck to check on the numerous icebergs. None offered a threat to the *Rotterdam*.

Another immigrant from Napoli recollected, *"How can a steerage passenger remember that he is a human being when he must first pick worms from his food, and eat in his stuffy, stinking bunk, or in the hot and fetid atmosphere of a compartment where one hundred fifty men sleep, or in juxtaposition to a seasick man?"* (4)

Besides seasickness, vomitus, spoiled food and a lack of ventilation in steerage, the voyage passed uneventfully.

A fellow traveler in a group of laborers spoke of the reason they left Italy. *"We would have eaten each other had we stayed."* (5) Marcello, Mario, Francesco and Rocco longed for America, to forget the old and start anew. Jobs, regular wages, the chance of wealth dominated the conversations as the days dragged on. On the twelfth day, after lunch, they heard a cry from above. Word quickly passed through the crowd. Land!

Running up on deck, Marcello and the passengers who were well enough strained to see. He heard the shout. "Look, there she is!"

The Statue of Liberty came into view, torch held high, facing the ship and welcoming the immigrants. With the *Rotterdam* making eleven knots steaming through the Verrazano Narrows, they entered New York Harbor. A harbor full of vessels teaming with immigrants waited to unload and be processed by immigration.

Francesco knew where to look. He turned and saw past the statue, pointing to Ellis Island. "Mia Dios."

An American crew- member explained to Francesco. "The old complex lasted from 1892 to 1897, when the old wooden structures on Ellis Island burnt to the ground. Entrance examinations for the last three years have been at the Barge Office in lower Manhattan. People say they were easier than on Ellis Island. You steerage passengers will be examined in comfort. These new brick buildings on Ellis Island were finished last year. They can handle this harborful of ships. They are used to large crowds."

The friends crowded around the crewman. Francesco asked, "Why do they make us take the test?"

"America does not allow sick passengers to enter."

"What is the test like?"

"The Progressives care only for your safety. A group of intellectuals designed the station to conform with modern theories. Diseased passengers are treated in an up to date hospital on the island. Translators circulate through the crowds. Food is provided for as long as the passengers are forced to remain. Don't worry. Only three percent of passengers are sent back home for health reasons."

Marcello looked beyond the renovated Ellis Island. "What is that railroad building?"

The crewman said, "That is the Jersey City terminus of the Central Jersey Railroad."

Marcello stared at the red brick building, bustling with people. "Where do they go?"

The crewman laughed. "Not everyone stays in New York. Some travel across the plains to places West. See the tower?"

Francesco said, "Yes, it is a beautiful clock."

"Americans must always know the time. Don't let time pass you by."

Francesco wondered, "Why do people chose to leave this beautiful area of New York. What could be better in Chicago, Philadelphia or the Wild West?"

"I don't know. Perhaps you will find out soon." The crewman said goodbye.

Marcello and his friends couldn't wait to see America. All they had to do was pass the test: the examinations on Ellis Island.

Marcello allowed hope to creep into his heart. Perhaps they were lucky and would not take the examination, with its risk of deportation. His hope increased as they steamed up the Hudson River past the Battery. Tugboats eased the *Rotterdam* into the Holland American Hoboken Piers, across the

Hudson River from mid-town Manhattan.

America!

They docked on January fourth 1902 as sleet pounded the decks. The first and second-class voyagers on the *Rotterdam III* passed their tests in the comfort of their staterooms and left with piles of luggage.

Ferries came around the starboard side for steerage class passengers. Marcello and his friends received instructions to collect their belongings and prepare to disembark to the ferries for their trip to the exam center. Marcello's hope dissolved. Fear gripped his heart. He would be tested on Ellis Island.

His group boarded the *General Putnam* ferry with one hundred other steerage passengers. An ancient barge, its owners made it look like a ferry to qualify for the lucrative immigrant business. There were no amenities and barely enough room for the passengers. Reversing course, they steamed down the Hudson for the seven-minute trip and docked at the main entrance to Ellis Island.

As Marcello got his land legs back, another passenger from Roma sank to his knees and kissed the ground. A loud official hustled the immigrants into the Main Building. "Leave all luggage outside in this pile. We will sort it out later."

What would become of their possessions? It was everything the new friends owned on earth. The four young Italians broke out in a nervous sweat.

Entering the imposing trellised entryway of Ellis Island's main building, another official pinned a number on Marcello's jacket, corresponding to his name on the *Rotterdam's* manifest. He pushed Marcello along towards the grand staircase at the front of the building.

Officials in white coats on the second floor observed the travelers making their way up the steep staircase. One picked on Francesco, chatting away to no one in particular in a mixture of English and Italian. The official wrote a letter in chalk on his jacket, and directed Francesco to a room separate from the others.

Marcello ascended the staircase and continued down the hall. "What happened to Francesco?" he whispered to Mario.

"I don't know, but it can't be good. I hope he doesn't get sent back."

"Do you think he failed the test already?" Rocco asked. No one replied.

They waited in a long room with a high ceiling. An official carrying a basket approached them. He gave each man a yellow fruit with a darker part to grasp on top, about a quarter of a meter long. The man demonstrated how to peel the yellow skin back. To Marcello's amazement, he took a bite of the white part and swallowed. "Banana," he said, throwing the yellow skin away in the trash.

Marcello gazed at this demonstration. The crewmember on the *Rotterdam* played a trick and Marcello didn't appreciate the gesture. He enjoyed the taste of his first American banana, though. His friends managed to thank the official for the snack, then laughed and pounded Marcello's back.

As Marcello, Rocco and Mario enjoyed the food, Francesco sweat. He waited with others in a small room. They had the same curious chalk mark on the lapel of their jackets. They seemed outgoing, but spoke different languages. Francesco guessed his neighbor spoke Russian. Another he knew to be Greek. A third man with a large hat might be speaking Turkish.

After an interminable wait, an official spoke to Francesco in Italian. "Sir, do you know what day it is?"

"Yes, it's Tuesday."

"Very good. What ship did you travel on?"

Francesco felt confused. Why did the official spend his time asking these inane questions? Didn't he have better things to do? "Why, the *Rotterdam*."

"Do you know where you are?"

"Yes, sir. This is Ellis Island, New York, in America. I do not know the name of this building." Now Francesco wondered about the sanity of this supposed official.

"Do you know any language besides Italian?"

"Well, sir, my uncle taught me a few words of English. But I am not fluent by any means," Francesco replied.

The official wiped off the mark from the jacket vest. "I fear there has been a mistake. Please continue down the hall and join your friends. Welcome to America."

After shaking hands with the official, Francisco ran down the corridor to rejoin his friends. At the doorway, he worried again as he spotted Mario, Rocco, Marcello and the others standing straight and tall. They were quite solemn and very naked. Doctors with stethoscopes listened and prodded and grunted.

Francisco watched as a doctor took out a metal instrument with a small hook on the end. He pulled on Marcello's eyelid and examined underneath. His eye did not fall into his pocket.

"Take off your clothes, Francesco," Marcello whispered. "The doctors must examine you. Then we will be free!"

Scratching his head, Francesco did as he was told. Soon, the examination ended. The men lined up and marched downstairs to another large, open room. They stood in a long, straight line facing a podium. There were ten such lines. The first in line answered questions from yet another official.

The friends conversed in whispers. "Francesco, what happened to you?"

"An official pulled me aside, marked my lapel, and led me to a room. Then, another official who spoke Italian asked me stupid questions. I didn't know what was the point. What a waste of the official's time. Finally, he learned I spoke English, and let me join you."

Marcello smiled. "I think he maybe thought you are crazy, the way you speak two languages at the same time." He laughed, but discreetly.

"Don't forget to tell them about the padroni," Francesco said.

"I didn't sign a contract," Marcello answered. "Do you think he'll let me, when we pass through?"

"I think it will be all right," his friend replied.

As time dragged, Marcello told about the strange, new banana they had given him, and how the inside part tasted very good. Finally, he reached the front of the line.

He figured out the operation. In front of each line stood a small podium, one of ten placed across the width of the room. Behind each podium stood an official in uniform of cap, black jacket and dark wool pants. Pen in hand, the official repeated a series of questions. They didn't vary, repeated endlessly to each immigrant.

"What is your name, sir?" The official spoke courteously in Italian.

"Marcello D'Alessandro, from Italy." He looked at the official, eyes wide. He broke out in sweat, partially from wearing two complete suits.

"Town of birth?"

"Salandra, in Basilicata. That is southern Italy, sir," Marcello replied, equally courteous.

"Are you a polygamist?" The official's pen hovered, poised for the answer.

Marcello felt at a loss. Finally, he said, "I don't even have one wife, much less several. Women are beautiful, but such a bother."

That brought a smile to the official's face. "Are you an anarchist?"

"What?"

"An anarchist."

"I believe in America, sir," Marcello said, unsure of the correct reply.

"Do you have a job?"

"Yes, sir, the padrone will meet us outside and bring us to our job."

"Very well, Mr. D'Alessandro. Welcome to America, and good luck. Next."

With that, Marcello walked forward, down the steps, and outside to the dock with his friends. They collected their baggage

The ride back to lower Manhattan on the *General Putnam* ferry felt different to Marcello. He was a free man! Joined by his fellow Contadini, they spent a minute comparing notes about their Ellis Island experience and breathing great gulps of sea air. To a man, they praised God for sparing them the rigors of Ellis Island and delivering them safely.

The friends embarking from the ferry in Lower Battery Park dressed as if in uniform in hats, dark trousers and dark jackets with white shirts. Wearing their best and only leather shoes, they looked smaller and darker than the New Yorkers milling about. They formed a distinct group, gazing around at the tall buildings, the many fine horse drawn wagons, and the people. Marcello said, "So many thousands of people. So crowded."

Here was an American man, obviously a workman by his dress, hurrying under a load of tools. There a fine couple, she in a frilly hat and long purple dress, holding the hand of a man in top hat, jacket and tie. He let go to buy flowers from a street side vendor, which he then presented to the lady with a bow and a flourish. So much to see. So many people passing by.

They heard a hail in Italian. "Hello. I am Luigi, the padrone."

Rocco and Mario introduced Marcello, and asked if he could join the work group.

"Yes, no problem. Are you hungry?"

No one wanted to stop to eat. They walked about the neighborhood, peppering the padrone with questions by the thousands. The padrone led them on a walk up Broadway, then towards the East Side till they arrived at a large building on Mott Street. Marcello counted at least six stories. Every window seemed to be covered with something, flowers, vegetables or sheets drying in the breeze.

Luigi made a ceremony at the entrance. "This is your new home in America. We will walk up the stairs and I will show you your room. Then I can answer your questions."

Walking past an outdoor privy, the men followed the padrone. After five flights of stairs, he opened the door to a clean, white, small room, the same size as their berth on the *Rotterdam*. The wide-open window allowed ventilation and cold air. Marcello leaned out to see the view, which consisted of the backside of another building.

The men sat on the floor. The padrone spoke in Italian. "Gentlemen, this is your sleeping quarters. Tomorrow, you will start your new job. Your have the privilege of helping New York City construct the greatest subway system in the world. Your wages are $1.25 a day. I will take $1 a day to repay your ship fare, food, hotel in France, and for this room. You will pay for your own food, unless you request a loan from me, which I will gladly offer at reasonable rates. What questions do you have?"

No one bothered with arithmetic in his head. There were no questions.

After the short talk and orientation to the neighborhood, the men followed the padrone downstairs. They decided to walk around the area. Luigi showed them the street signs, read them the advertisements for businesses and shops, and gave general directions and a tour. As they headed for a restaurant the padrone recommended, Francesco saw a handbill posted on a telephone pole and stopped.

"What does it say?" Mario asked. His curiosity wasn't dulled by fatigue.

"It is for laborers to build a water reservoir for New York City," Francesco read out loud to them.

"Common labor, white- $1.30 to $1.50.

Common labor, colored- $1.25 to $1.40.

Common labor, Italian- $1.15 to $1.25." (6)

Mario thought a moment and said, "It seems that our padrone has started us off with the normal wage. He is a fair and just man."

After a hearty Italian dinner, paid for by the padrone, the nervous excitement and energy abated. Marcello and his friends found their way to the room. They fell into a deep sleep, dreaming of a pot of gold at the other end. They were willing to work for that pot of gold. Nothing could stop them now. They reached America, the Promised Land.

*

March seventeenth 1902, St. Patrick's Day dawned on New York City. The men worked like slaves for three and a half months in America. The padrone told them he would bring a bucket of green bire to their room after work. Before the party came another long shift.

They fell into their daily routine. The men entered the subway shaft. The ten Italian compatriots joined ninety other Italian laborers and one supervisor on the short train. In two minutes they arrived at their destination, underground at the end of the shaft. Although cooler than on the surface of Broadway, mud covered the floor of the shaft. Foul smells assaulted their senses. The air felt dank.

Picks and shovels unloaded, the men followed the direction of the foreman and started digging. Dust filled the air. The men coughed and gagged. Their ten man Italian crew, experienced in subway building, toiled rapidly, breaking the ground sixty feet below Broadway. Filth covered their bodies by the first hour, sweat streaking their faces like war paint. The leaking water and humidity caused their joints to ache. Carts lifted the dirt back on the train for use as landfill. This load went with all the others to Ellis Island so the facilities could expand to include a larger hospital and infectious disease ward.

Mario, muscular and well fed, had pallor in his dark skin. "I tire of this. Six months and I only save twenty-five cents a day for six days a week, ten hours a day. Sometimes I think there is no way out, that we labor forever to pay off our debts. Sometimes I think the padrone takes advantage and takes too much."

Another disagreed. *"We are ignorant and do not know English. Our boss brought us here, knows where to find work, makes contracts with the companies. What should we do without him?"* (7)

Marcello, leaning on his pick, listened and considered the comments. "You are right. We knew nothing of New York when we were at home. It was best we sign with the padrone. We had no job, no place to live. Now things have changed. We work like dogs and do not complain. The padrone takes nearly everything, and then tells us the rent is more expensive. We have paid him back ten times over for his support. It's time for a change."

Francesco stopped working and looked at Marcello. His voice quaked. "What do you mean? Do you have a plan?"

Watching for the foreman, Marcello pulled out a rolled up paper from his pocket. As the men gathered around in the dim electric light, he showed his copy of *L'Eco d'Italia,* (The Voice of Italy) the popular Italian language newspaper they read. "The newspaper's editor, Mr. G. F. Secchi de Casali, supports a better life for Italian immigrants. He supports a farming settlement in south New Jersey. Land is cheap, plentiful and produces wondrous crops. Listen to what Mr. Barretta, an Italian farmer, wrote to Italian immigrants several years ago:

The climate in Vineland is similar to that in the central part of Italy. The spring here comes earlier than the spring in any other central region of the United States. Here grapevines, many varieties of fruit, and many agricultural products grow in abundance while the land does not require very hard work because it is easily broken.'

'It is the ideal place for Italians who, instead of working under oppressive and dangerous conditions in mines or in other manual labor with the danger of being assaulted by the Irish or of losing their jobs or businesses, could establish a pleasant and lucrative situation for themselves by buying five, ten, or twenty acres of land in Vineland and paying on easy payment plans.' (8) Vineland, my friends."

"What's going on there?" the foreman shouted. He ran towards them, raising his arm. "We don't pay you to stand around and talk. Get back to work."

"Yes, sir," Mario said. "Sorry, sir."

Marcello whispered, "We'll speak more of this later." They returned to their backbreaking labor with a smile on their lips and renewed hope in their hearts.

Turn of the century Vineland held an attraction for those immigrants trapped in manufacturing and manual labor in New York City.

Marcello educated the men about Vineland after work that day. Located in south central New Jersey about one hundred fifty miles from New York, in a pleasant climatic zone with good soil, it started as a vision of a "Utopian" community. Charles K. Landis wished to attract men with ambition and determination, regardless of their educational achievements. Landis wrote, *"I wanted land more adapted to fruit than to grain, because, to grow grain and stock would require much more capital than to raise fruit, and the rate of profit on stock would be much smaller. In short, fruit culture was better adapted to the kind of town and colony that I wished to found."* (9)

Landis dabbled as a land speculator and developer before and after his efforts in Vineland. In the 1860's, attracted by Landis' New York newspaper ads, New England farmers started settling the area. They found the ads true, that a man could cultivate and with hard work make a living selling fruit and vegetables to nearby Philadelphia and New York, two of the largest markets in the United States. Landis then tried to attract Irish settlers but was unsuccessful.

In the 1870's, Italians started to settle the area. An Italian connection developed in 1872, when Carlo Quairoli, Italian patriot under Garibaldi, moved to Vineland and purchased considerable property. He brought his family in 1877, aiding Landis in establishing a large Italian settlement. Quairoli's connections with the Italian government gave the area legitimacy, and his extensive written report on Vineland to the Italian government received wide publicity and circulation in the home country.

The major force pulling families from New York to Vineland was the handbills and editorials of G. F. Secchi de Casali, starting in 1874. In the employ of Landis, Casali kept a steady diet of news from Vineland to the Italian speakers of New York City.

The colony had legitimate goals and played fairly with its finances. The climate remained moderate, the soil fertile. Crops found a ready market in New York and Philadelphia. No liquor stores or bars ensured a quiet environment for raising children. Dr. Thomas B. Welch joined the movement, starting the Welch Grape Juice Company to cater to the teetotalers.

Vineland had another advantage. Italian was used everywhere. With so many Italian immigrants, they didn't feel like a discriminated minority.

Landis planned a slice of Utopia. Manhattan's manual labor grew tiresome. The padrone took all the money. Why not try Vineland?

Later that evening of St. Patrick's Day 1902, when the padrone brought the green beer to the men, the mood improved. Rather than ten dispirited paupers, the padrone addressed a spirited team. The Italians felt their dreams, so long forgotten, awaken. The friends discussed their hopes for a better life, those happy plans of riches and freedom.

At the appropriate time, after the beer, Marcello stood. Speaking in broken English and Italian, he addressed the padrone. "Thank you, padrone, for all the aid and counsel you have given me over the last months. I never could have prospered in America without you. You gave me a job and a place to stay in this big city of New York. You showed me how to live in America and become a part of it. Now, padrone, it is time for a change. I will leave this house, with whoever wishes to join me, for a new job and a new room. I will pay you what is fair for this month's rent, but I will not pay you forever. Thank you again for your help, kind sir."

As Marcello sat, Luigi walked about, gauging the pulse of the room. As padrone, if he lost control of these workers, he could lose his own lucrative job. His power came from controlling large numbers of strong, cheap laborers that didn't know any better. His livelihood depended on controlling these ignorant peasants. He stared down at them, sitting on their haunches, drinking his beer. Few of the ten looked him in the eye. The others bowed their heads, save Francesco, Rocco and Mario. They stared at him in solidarity with Marcello.

He marked the troublemakers. "You men have worked very hard in your new jobs. The supervisor speaks highly of you. You should be proud."

He looked directly into Marcello's eyes, sneering. "When you signed the contract long ago in far away Italia, you promised to pay for all the padrone does for you. Transportation across the ocean, food, a steady job and housing has been given to you. However, you owe on rent. You break your sacred contract, leaving the padrone to pay your bill, and walk away. If you do this, you betray me. You are no man, you are an animal. Now, make up your mind. Who will stay and work to honor their contract and their sacred word?"

No one spoke.

"This is how you repay your debt?"

Marcello stood. "Yes. We go."

"You are no longer welcome. Do not return. Do not rely on my kindness any longer. You are animals to do this. Your families will hear of this, back in Italy."

Marcello looked to his friends. Slowly, Mario followed. Everyone else looked at the floor. "I'm sorry it must end this way, padrone. To my close friends, the best of times awaits us. Goodbye and God bless."

Marcello and Mario left the room and their old life.

On the street, Mario wiped his brow. "I'm sorry Francesco and Rocco didn't join us. Now what have you gotten us into?"

"We are free," Marcello answered, peering up and down Broadway, still crowded with drunken Irish revelers. "We have no debt. We have money in our pockets. We are young and strong. Let's celebrate by finding a new home. Tomorrow, a new job, where we can save quickly and move to Vineland. Only when we own our land and profit for ourselves will we fulfill our dreams. Come, Mario, don't you want to be free, and rich?"

Smiling, Mario replied, "Of course, Marcello."

Months later the roommates met Francesco and Rocco on Broadway. Mario punched their arms. "How are you, my friends?"

"We work on the subway. No savings, no better off," Francesco replied. "How are you getting along with your plan to farm?"

Marcello summed up their efforts. "We still look for a farm."

Sitting at an outdoor restaurant in warm sunshine, the old friends shared a glass of vino. Francesco and Rocco badgered him. "Tell us, do you save money?"

"A little."

"What is it like working above the ground?"

Marcello drank his wine. He patted his lips with the napkin and lit a cigarette. "A job opened on an assembly line. I learned the skills the first day, then sat down and concentrated for ten hours a day, day after day. Hot, tough work at a milk chocolate factory. The boss did not wish to stop the assembly line for any reason. One day, I got distracted and bent over to tie my shoe. Chocolate, paper and sugar oozed off the table and dripped to the floor. I realized I'd made a mistake and tried to catch them with my hands. Mario came over to help. Nothing worked. Drenched in milk chocolate, I yelled, 'Stop the line.' After a big mess piled up on the floor, the supervisor flipped the switch. He was not happy with the chocolate or me. I almost lost my job because of my shoe."

"Your shoe!" Francesco and Rocco almost fell off their chairs laughing. "A toast to your shoe."

The men yelled "Salute" and drank.

Marcello leaned over and whispered. "The next month Mario and I worked at a sugar factory. They paid better. Living in a tiny room in another tenement on Mott Street helped us save three-quarters of our $1.30 per hour wages. I'm a cook and enjoyed making meals and eating at home. Our lives have changed a little, but we are just as happy without a padrone. We take English lessons and improve, work, and walk the streets of Manhattan for pleasure. I'm glad we ran into you fellows today. We feel like Americans."

Rocco hung his head. "I'm glad for your success. You prosper, we pay the padrone. Perhaps we should have left with you. We may never leave till the entire city is crossed with subways. I hope to see you again soon. Good luck, may God be with you."

"Goodbye," Mario yelled. When they were out of earshot, he commented, "Looks like you and I did the right thing. Our gamble paid off."

The men retired to their room on Mott Street. On the way in, a neighbor called to Marcello. He had a visitor from Italy.

Marcello ran up the stairs. Waiting outside in the hallway sat his brother, his best childhood friend Giovanni D'Alessandro.

"Giovanni, such a surprise. I'm so glad to see you."

Giovanni hugged his brother. "I have a message from father."

Marcello grimaced. "What does he want?"

"Convince Marcello to return, to re-unite the family."

"Giovanni, come in and eat with us. Then we will talk."

At the home cooked meal that first evening in the tenement, Giovanni seemed more rigid than as a youth. Giovanni spoke with passion, gripping his brother by the shoulders. Tears streamed down his cheeks. Ramrod straight, he cried, prodded and begged, all for the sake of their parents and the family, 'la famiglia.' "Thank you for the food, Marcello. You have learned well. I must ask you to return home! It is your duty. Your father begs, pleads with you. For the love of God."

Marcello, though happy to see his brother, could not believe the message. "I want nothing to do with Italy. When father forbade me to see Donata, my decision was final. He understood."

Giovanni clutched his brother's arm. "Marcello, for our mother, then."

Marcello cried. "My life is here. I'm an American now. I'm about to complete the last part of my plan. We move to Vineland, a beautiful agricultural community away from this crowded city. We farm and enjoy life."

"But you can farm in Salandra."

Marcello showed Giovanni the Italian newspaper articles so he would believe and understand.

Giovanni nodded. "I recognize the place. The same ads are found in Potenza and Matera back home. They sound like you have an easier life here than in Salandra."

The brothers drank wine. They spent several days together, reminiscing about their youth, arguing about Italy. Marcello's resolve remained intact.

Giovanni realized the futility of his journey. He booked passage on a steamship. On a rainy afternoon, they took a ferry across the Hudson. Marcello waited at the gate.

Giovanni took his younger brother in his arms. "I fear I will never see you again."

"That is true, unless you come here to visit. You are always welcome. I will not be visiting Italy."

"Then this is goodbye, brother."

Marcello shook his hand. He pulled an envelope from his pocket. "Please, Giovanni, deliver this letter to Donata."

Marcello stood tall, convinced of the righteousness of his path.

Giovanni said goodbye and returned to the old country, her problems, and family. When Giovanni arrived in Salandra and gave their father the news, it broke his heart. He never recovered from the shock.

Giovanni completed his brother's wish. He delivered Marcello's letter to Donata

A

CHAPTER SEVEN

IN VINO, VERITAS

Vineland, New Jersey, 1902. Was Landis's vision an illusion of Utopia, or the reality of freedom?

In May of 1902, Mario and Marcello planned their trip to Vineland for Saturday. Mario thought of it as the fulfillment of a dream. Marcello felt it began a new era in life.

Friday, Marcello received mail from Italy, a return letter from Donata Onorato Albano. He'd felt foolish weeks ago, sending it with Giovanni. He couldn't help himself. He remained obsessed. His excuse for the message was a godfather's questions about his godson. He still retained that role in Donata's life.

His gamble paid off. What the letter said, though terrible, made his heart leap. Passions from long ago returned.

The next morning they ate breakfast at home. The odor, though pleasant, permeated everything in the small room. Not that they had much. Two used chairs, a kerosene stove, candles. No running water or toilet facilities, no paint, no decorations. Marcello's wardrobe consisted of the two suits he emigrated with, and a work outfit of rough but sturdy cloth. The bright May morning sunshine entered through their solitary window, slightly open to allow a draft. Marcello folded the letter away and turned to Mario. "It's time to travel. I checked the arrangements. It's a short ferry across the Hudson to the Central New Jersey Railroad terminus. Then, one hundred fifty miles by electric train to Vineland. I want to check on the price of farm land."

Mario agreed. The heat and humidity of summer approached. Escape from the city gave welcome relief.

The friends walked through deserted lower Manhattan to the docks. Few stirred on a Sunday morning. Boarding the fine commercial ferry, they gazed across the Hudson to New Jersey. Mario reminisced about their first ferry on the Hudson, the *General Putnam*, and their ordeal at Ellis Island. They breathed clean ocean air.

The beauty of the Central New Jersey Railroad station buoyed their spirits. Abutting the shoreline, six ferry docks awaited passengers at the station. They debarked, and a one-minute walk brought them to the front of the red brick railway terminus building. The spire held a fine timepiece. *Tempus fugit* read the inscription. Time flies. Signs and maps allowed the travelers to pick the correct train. Marcello bought tickets. Behind the concourse, filled with people of all nations and languages, a corrugated roof protected patrons as they boarded the trains. Marcello glanced at the maps to Chicago, Philadelphia, Denver and San Francisco. He could travel anywhere in the country from here.

In a cloud of smoke, the train pulled from the station, leaving the buildings of lower Manhattan behind. Marcello unfolded his letter, read it, smiled, and refolded it a dozen times. Gazing out the window, he daydreamed of better times, a farm, a wife, and freedom. He and Mario rode in comfort through Camden, to south-central New Jersey. Before he knew it, the train pulled up to a beautiful park with shade trees dotting the grassy acres. An open pavilion served as the terminal of the Western Jersey Railroad in Vineland.

"You see?" asked Marcello.

Mario regarded his friend. His jaw hung slack but his eyes beamed. "Beautiful! Very lush, and no mountains to wash away topsoil."

"Trees, open space. Did you notice all the farms outside of town?"

"For miles all around."

Marcello looked at his friend. "It's perfect! Let's take a walk and survey the place."

Leaving the quiet park with its manicured grass and walkways, Marcello led the way towards Landis Avenue. The wide thoroughfare with its trees lining each side made a favorable impression. Neat, small storefronts displayed a variety of goods. After several blocks, he came across a Catholic Church named Sacred Heart Parish, and stopped in to say a prayer.

After that brief visit, Marcello took his friend by the shoulders. "This is the town. I'm to become a farmer and own my land. What do you say, Mario?

Are you with me?"

"Let's ask this man on the sidewalk. He looks Italian, and dressed like a farmer. We don't know how much is everything."

They chatted on the sidewalk of Landis Avenue, across from Sacred Heart, just outside a restaurant. Several horse drawn carts passed down the dirt road. Striking up a conversation, the friendly man who called himself Tomaso volunteered a wealth of information. An inch taller than Marcello, thin and dark, with leathery skin, he wore glasses on his nose. But he dressed in the familiar farming clothes of Italy. He confirmed the soil was fertile, the climate pleasant. Tomaso said the market for goods in Philadelphia and New York was strong. "They pay a fair price for healthy fruit and vegetables."

"Tomaso, my friend. How is the price of land here in Vineland?"

Tomaso nodded. "In the beginning it seems like too much. Twenty dollars an acre."

"So much? Are you sure?"

Tomaso waved his hand. "Yes, my friend. But you can get a loan. Please join me for lunch at my favorite restaurant on Landis Avenue. You can ask my friends your questions."

Opening the door, Tomaso introduced the strangers. The entire restaurant filled with Italians. Most of them worked in town, and let their wives and children tend the land. Only on Saturdays did the men have time to work the fields. Tomaso explained their philosophy. "My friends, that's what children are for, to help their parents. Don't be discouraged. You can borrow money for the land at good rates. The profit on your farm goods will allow you to pay it off and buy more land. Everyone in the restaurant did this."

"When you clear the land and fell the trees, what happens?" Mario asked. "We have floods and erosion in Basilicata."

One of the farmers laughed. Tomaso smiled. "You must be from the mountains. We are on a flat plain here. The soil stays with us. We freshen it with manure and vegetable matter. It is very fertile. If you have time, I can take you to my farm and show off the quality of fruit we grow."

"Thank God," Marcello said. "I don't want the money I pay for land to run down the river to the sea. Are people friendly to Italians here?"

"That is not a problem. It is not like the discrimination in New York. We have over five hundred Italian families. Life is peaceful here. Everyone gets the same wage at the shoe factory, unless you are a supervisor."

Marcello and Mario grinned as they finished their lunch. The Italians like Tomaso were nice to them.

All too soon, the men left to catch their train. Tomaso walked them back to the park and the train station.

In the Old Italian style, the men embraced. Marcello dried a tear. "Thank you, friend. The information makes me determined to come again. Next time, I will be your neighbor."

On the train as they approached New York, Marcello re-read the letter from Donata Onorato Albano. *I feared I would never hear from you again. When you left Salandra so quickly my heart broke. I married Pasquale Albano as an obedient daughter should, but my heart belonged to you. Then we had Rocco, your godson. I'm pleased that you accepted the responsibility to be his godfather. He is growing into a fine child, almost three now. Life was good until several months ago. My husband left us.*"

"*I didn't know what to do with my life till your letter came, Marcello. Now, it seems like a gift from heaven. I am free from my parent's commands. If you are so inclined, I could travel to America and meet you. Please, let me know your wishes. I pray you feel the same of me as I do for you. Love, Donata.*"

His obsession, his independence, his struggles coalesced into this decision. Nearing Jersey City, Marcello woke his friend. "Mario, I've made up my mind. I'm moving to Vineland. I'll get a job in town to support my family, and save enough for a farm. Will you join me?"

The train rolled through populated neighborhoods near the terminal. The lights of New York shone across the water, beckoning. Mario hesitated. "My friend, I haven't saved as much money as you. The prices are too high. And I don't have a family to work the farm. As I remember, neither do you, Marcello. How will you work the land?"

Marcello read Donata's letter. "So, I will move to Vineland with a family, rent a small place, and buy two acres of land, perhaps with an option to buy more. I will have Donata and my godson Rocco, and we will live together forever. I will work in town during the week, and on the weekends I will supervise the farm, growing fruits and vegetables, and perhaps grapes for wine. If I could make the poor land of Salandra grow, it should be easy in Vineland."

"I'm not sure I'm ready to join you, Marcello."

Marcello gripped his friend's arm. They experienced so many things together since their immigration. "Please think about it, Mario. This is a wonderful opportunity. Good luck, whatever you choose. I must do this now. Donata is waiting for my letter."

Donata and little Rocco planned their emigration in summer, 1902 after a favorable reply to her letter. Donata found it difficult saying goodbye to her family. She lingered in the arms of her favorite sister Rosaria. Donata would miss her sister's company. After tears and the good-byes she was ready. She carried two bags stuffed with clothing and other prized remembrances of home, and sat on the cart, waving slowly, tears streaming down her cheeks, sure of two things. She desired a new life with Marcello. And she would miss her favorite sister desperately.

Pasquale Albano never returned to Salandra. Donata didn't give him another thought.

Rocco smiled and enjoyed the cart. The horse drawn cart rolled down the hill to the main road between Salandra and Napoli, where they picked up several others from Calciano. From there they traveled west, the main road to the coast. The ride to Napoli dragged on. They stopped in each village. Donata relaxed, glad to have a day off from the hard life of the farm. She listened to the other women, all young and strong like her. Some had babies. They helped each other care for the children. Most of the women traveled with their husbands. The majority of the men traveled alone.

After twelve hours in the cart, the group arrived at a hotel in Napoli. Donata and Rocco walked to the *Opera Assistenza Emigranti* (Emigrant Aid Office) before bedtime that evening. She made arrangements for passage in steerage and meals during the voyage on the ship. The next morning they followed Marcello's path and sailed to America.

The Mediterranean Sea remained peaceful. No one in steerage had ever experienced the rocking of a ship. They made an uneventful voyage, which made eating a bit easier. Donata had pre-paid their meals. The cook in steerage tried to extort a bribe from her and other passengers, withholding lunch the first day. Protesting, the immigrants raised a ruckus, and when the cook resisted, they threatened him with bodily harm. There were no further incidents.

The travelers, those that didn't become seasick, enjoyed thin soup, bread and soggy vegetables three times a day, if they felt well enough to eat. On Sunday they got herring.

After passage through the Straits of Gibraltar the seas changed. Waves were higher and the wind picked up. Donata suffered seasickness. Ten days later, after crossing in good weather, Marcello arrived at Ellis Island. He waited at the "kissing post," an area where relatives from the states were first allowed to re-unite with loved ones. Since Marcello, a male with a job, waited for his family, their examination was cursory, the questions superficial. Donata and

Rocco joined the ranks of new Americans.

On the clear sunny day, without stopping in New York, they boarded the ferry to the Central New Jersey train station and traveled to their new home in Vineland.

Marcello spoke in whispers as they approached the little green park with the pavilion that served as the Vineland station. Marcello stepped down from the train, held little Rocco and waited for Donata to descend. She looked even more beautiful than he remembered. Her traditional peasant skirt, dark blouse and white halter wrap across her breasts and around the waist reminded him of the old country. Her hair and the strong bearing of her back filled Marcello with pride. How thin!

Her long black hair and dark eyes set off her narrow face. Marcello's heart raced. Their reunion at the kissing post boded well for the future. As a proud Italian, he didn't show public display of affection. Marcello's happiness with his one true love, his Donata, showed through his voice as he spoke of Vineland. He picked up Rocco, his godson, and kissed the boy on the cheek. They hit it off immediately.

Chatting in Italian, the new family walked four short blocks from the Vineland terminal to Quincy Street. Marcello opened the door to their tiny rental house. "Rocco, you are tired. Here is your bed. Time for a nap."

The lovers had a formal reunion after so many miles, so long ago.

After their tryst, Marcello couldn't contain his enthusiasm. "Let us visit our humble farm."

Donata, Rocco and Marcello turned left, away from Landis Avenue, and strolled in the summer sun.

"This is a beautiful village, Marcello. Everyone speaks Italian. I like it." Donata squeezed his arm.

The pavement ended and the road turned to dirt. A man in a cart called out. "Is that you, Marcello?"

"Hello, Tomaso. We are here to stay. I'm taking the family to see my acres."

"So, this is the lovely woman you spoke about, Marcello."

"Yes, she is the love of my life. Donata, say hello to Tomaso."

She smiled at the tall Italian farmer.

"Please, won't you ride with me?" Tomaso picked up Rocco, the parents climbed in after the boy. They completed the trip in comfort, riding on hay and chatting about the old country. Marcello and Donata smiled as Rocco sat in the middle, making sounds to the horse.

Arriving at his two acres, Marcello bid goodbye to Tomaso. He outlined his plan to Donata. "We work together on the weekends. We will work our way to a good life. After breaking ground and planting cash crops, our life will improve."

Donata stood beside him, silent.

"I'll reserve one side for grape—vines, since they take several years to yield suitable grapes. I think Cabernet Sauvignon, Pinot Noir, Merlot and Cabernet Franc grapes are suitable. Soon, these woods will become fields, sprouting peaches, tomatoes and numerous other fruits and vegetables. My grapes will turn into fine wine."

Donata nodded. "It sounds wonderful, Marcello. Don't you think, Rocco?" She held the boy tightly, shaking with the enormity of her new life.

Marcello continued his dream. "After the fall harvest, we can take a holiday to New York or Philadelphia to sell the bounty. Soon, they will be rich, free and happy. As I pay the debt, I can start to make wine."

His story persuaded Donata, allaying her fears of this new country and its strange customs. After the tour of their farm, Donata had one request. They walked back to Landis Avenue and made their way to the empty Sacred Heart Church. She kneeled on the altar with him, alone, exchanging ersatz vows. "Swear we are married in the eyes of God. That we will love and respect each other, in sickness and health, till death."

Marcello humored her. "Yes, it is as you say. Don't worry, things will work out. Later, we will formalize the union."

-

The new family settled in the rental house. Each day, Donata brought Rocco down the dirt path and cleared the fields. Marcello joined them on the weekend. The first meager crop yielded little cash. The next year's improved considerably. After that, they prospered. Their small brown, unassuming rental house on Quincy Street, along a quiet dirt road in the Italian residential neighborhood, turned into a home. The Italian community of Vineland accepted them lovingly, and they never lacked for socializing or entertainment.

The couple worked hard and invested everything in the farm. Marcello had plenty of time to reflect on his new life in America, driving the horse drawn wagon for the Keighley Shoe Company from Monday to Friday. He didn't mind the boredom of driving the cart. It allowed him to escape the hard farm labor and make money to pay off their debt. Regular hours offered escape from domestic turmoil. As he made his rounds, gently prodding the horse, he had but one regret.

Donata's health suffered.

In 1905 she bore Margharita, their first child together. After her birth they expanded the farm to five acres.

Dominic came in 1906, and they added another five acres. By this time, the four varietal grapes matured, and Marcello sealed several casks of wine for aging.

Donata never complained about the farming. Back home in Italy, that would be a man's job, but Marcello explained the differences in the economy of the United States. She took the children along. They helped her weed and hoe and pick the crops.

At home in the evening, Donata tired. "I made supper, Marcello. I can't stay awake. Please put the babies to bed."

"Donata, are you ill?"

"No, just tired. My stomach hurts. Hurry to bed with me."

Marcello kissed her. She shook in his arms. "Is it from Pasquale Albano's treatment?"

"I don't know, Marcello. I've always been nervous. All my sisters told me. Goodnight."

Marcello didn't remember her as nervous. She'd lost weight and often couldn't eat. She tried, but her farm work deteriorated. She lost interest in events outside her family.

Cursing her former husband and his cowardly actions, Marcello put the babies to bed. Sleeping next to Donata, he struggled to find a solution.

He had no cure.

When Frank was born in 1908, Marcello and Donata owned twenty acres. He decided not to buy more land. It was enough for the two of them, plus Rocco turned eleven. Marcello gathered the family at the kitchen table. He believed in the Italian saying, *"Una mazza, lavoro e pane fanno I figli belli."* A cane, work, and bread make for fine children. No need for schooling. "Donata, Rocco is big enough. He can start to help you full time. No more school. You need more rest."

"But Marcello, he's so young."

"I worked at his age."

Donata looked away. "I hoped, since we moved to America, that he could learn…things in school."

Marcello shook his head.

"I could use the help. Rocco, tomorrow you and I work the field."

Increasing productivity on the farm allowed the growing family to buy a small house on Second and Cherry Street. They moved two blocks into the central Italian community. Hardwood floors squeaked with the sound of so many children. South facing, the kitchen allowed sunshine into their lives at dinner. Marcello constructed the kitchen table and an easy chair by hand in his shop. They spoke their native language with all the neighbors. Everyone helped watch children like one big family.

Outside their front door, the city posted signs in English and Italian. *DO NOT CUT DOWN THE TREES.* Former owners on the block had cut down shade trees to plant a garden. The family had planted a small fruit tree in its place. The D'Alessandro family had plentiful food because of their personal efforts on the farm. Marcello continued his job driving the cart for the Keighley shoe factory during the week to keep cash flowing even in winter.

God blessed the family with Rosie in 1910. Donata formed a unique attachment with her baby. She felt so blessed by the child she wrote home to Salandra, to her sister Rosaria. In vivid detail, she described her life, the fertile ground and open spaces. It almost sounded like Salandra, without the poverty. "Rosaria, please consider my request. Join us in Vineland. Tell momma she is welcome too."

As Marcello read the letter, he closed his eyes. The letter painted a beautiful picture, a fairy tale.

Marcello experienced a different reality.

Donata's health failed.

A

CHAPTER EIGHT

AN ILL WIND
Vineland, 1912

By good fortune and the hard work of Donata, the Onorato sisters kept in touch over the years. Rosaria Onorato married Pasquale Iurlaro in Salandra in 1907. Two years later, their first baby arrived. By a terrible act of God, the baby developed diphtheria and died the following year. The sisters commiserated over that loss, through letters sent by ship.

Setting aside her grief, Rosaria pressed Pasquale Iurlaro for another baby. He agreed, except for one stipulation. He would emigrate to Vineland to buy a farm, get a job in town and set up a house. Convinced by Donata's letters that Vineland outshone Salandra, he insisted. Plus, he feared the tremors of a new European war. Better he should settle in America. Then he would send for Rosaria and they could complete their family.

Rosaria hadn't dared to dream. Knowing she'd be near her favorite sister made the time pass quickly. Pasquale emigrated in 1912. He received a warm welcome from Marcello and Donata. Working in the glass factory, he earned enough to send for Rosaria in 1913.

Rosaria Onorato Iurlaro received the letter with joy in her heart. Rosaria considered asking the rest of her family, Felicia, Francesco, Leonarada, Giuseppe and Maria to join them. At the last minute, she thought better of it. She must ask her husband for permission first. Wouldn't that be perfect, to unite the family again in America.

She boarded the steamship in Naples in June. Fine weather made for a rapid passage. When she arrived in America, in Vineland, she would have her husband and many more children. She could be near her dearest sister, Donata. They would be soul mates again, like in the old country.

Pasquale met her at Ellis Island. He didn't waste time keeping his promise. Rosaria became pregnant almost immediately. They moved into a two-story apartment just down Cherry Street from the D'Alessandro's. That proximity to her sister was the only cross in Rosaria's life.

Rosaria saw the decline in her sister that the letters didn't relate. Donata's new baby, Annette, born in 1912, seemed to break her mother's spirit. Rosaria did her best to help, cheering her sister with stories and helping with the six children. She listened to the constant tale of woe flowing from her sister.

The contrast in her sister's home felt overwhelming. Rosaria had a perfect life with the perfect husband. As a dutiful wife, she gave her husband pleasure, kept house and brought in extra money by cleaning and darning clothes. It was a peaceful, pleasant existence.

She looked down the street at Second and Cherry and saw her sister, a richer, busier sister whose mind and body played cruel tricks, dulling an otherwise idyllic existence. Rosaria prayed for her sister's salvation. What else could she do but pray to God?

Marcello worked with the vines in his spare time. After training Rocco, the farming chores eased. The grapes matured. Each week of the year he strode down the straight lines of stakes. He fondled the blossoming grape—vines. Each vine grew in a full circle around each stake, up, up towards the sun, which gave them robust flavor. Years of pruning the vines, hours spent picking grapes in the hot sun came to fruition. He polished his technique of winemaking. Precise measurement of the yeast. Refined timing of the mix. Sturdy oak casks to store the wine for aging. He loved every aspect of the process.

"Donata, after dinner we will decant the first cask of wine. Please join me."

She arrived after washing the dishes. He grew the grapes himself, built the oak casks by hand. He tried the local offerings and knew his wine outshone them. Marcello wiped the sweat from his palms. Standing in his small, damp cellar under the house, surrounded by ten wine casks, he initiated the ceremony.

Uncorking the first stimulated memories. His wife and son had thrown off their shoes and stomped and pressed the grapes, yielding grape juice mixed with the dark colored skins. He had poured the poudice into vats and added malolactic yeast. Measuring the sugar, estimated at twenty- three Brix, he determined an alcohol content of fourteen percent would result. Hand shaking, Marcello felt his fine oak casks. He'd sealed them with wax and a cork. He agonized about the waiting. A necessary evil, he wanted a fine wine with a balance between acid content, very dry with little residual sugar, and softening of the tannins to give an aged feel on the palate.

"Donata, Rocco, this isn't sfuso like we made in the old country. This product will sell to the fine restaurants in New York."

They smelled, sipped, spit. The family repeated the process for each of the ten casks. All except Marcello, who drank great gulps. The bouquet, legs, and above all the taste. The components possessed a fine balance. The oak aged the tannins beautifully. God blessed him with a miracle.

He looked to Donata.

She had a bad day with fatigue. She didn't like to drink the last several years. "Perhaps a little more aging. Very good, a touch bitter, a little more aging and it will be perfect."

Rocco saw a flash in his stepfather's eye. "Very nice. As fine as any restaurant on Landis Avenue."

Marcello's joy deflated. He sat down on his casks. "Thank you. You may go. I have more work to prepare the wine."

He wasn't satisfied with their critique of the wine. Did they have no feelings? Betrayed! Again!

After ten glasses he sat alone with his thoughts. He'd made good wine, although not quite ready for the finest New York restaurants. For him to spend more time, he'd need more children to help Donata and Rocco tend the vines. Marcello wished to devote more effort to the wine. Farming was too tiresome for someone with his talents. The job with the shoe factory bored him. Wine was truth! Wine was his answer.

Baby Elizabeth came to Donata in 1913. She planned a special celebration for the christening. The Baptism would be a dual rite, for her sister Rosaria birthed Rosa at nearly the same time.

At the Church of the Sacred Heart, the priest dressed in his ceremonial garb. Candles lit the interior, casting deep shadows. Children's shoes on the marble floor shattered the quiet. Parents and children alike dressed in their Sunday finest. Marcello helped Donata hold Elizabeth on the left of the baptismal font. Rosaria and Pasquale Iurlaro stood on the right, cuddling Rosa.

The priest intoned the words of the sacred Latin rite. "I baptize you in the name of the Father, and of the Son, and of the Holy Spirit." After the sign of the cross on the head, he poured water to cleanse the babies of original sin. The Sacrament completed, the families left to celebrate. The D'Alessandro clan made too much noise to remain in Church.

They walked to the D'Alessandro's house. Donata cooked, served the food and kept the children in line with a minimum of noise. Marcello spoke of his wine. Pasquale and Rosaria sat outside at a picnic table, where Marcello brought glasses of his best bouquets. He requested another opinion. "Please, Pasquale, try this. Aged for five years. From my first mature crop in Vineland. Rosaria, you also. Come, it's a special occasion. We won't be able to make children forever. But surely we will always enjoy wine. Come enjoy this with me."

Pasquale, a small, powerful man of abstemious tastes, sipped and swallowed. He was known as a man of few words. He worked hard at the glass factory, and planted a small plot of his own for vegetables to use at home.

"What do you think, Pasquale?"

"Very good. Thank you. I am honored. Allow me to get some cheese at our home. It will go well with the wine."

Marcello turned to his sister-in-law, Rosaria. At four feet eleven inches, she stood shorter than Marcello's chest. Childbirth put a few pounds on her hips. Looking at Rosaria, Marcello saw the principle difference from his wife. Rosaria smiled with a gleam in her eyes, a twinkle of enjoyment. Donata always looked sad. "What is your opinion, Rosaria?"

She sat in a small wooden chair in the back yard. A warm breeze ruffled the leaves. Soft grass below muffled the sound of children running about, and allowed Rosaria to walk barefoot. Gently lifting the stemmed glass, she sniffed. She rolled the wine around her glass and watched it ever so slowly roll down to the bottom. Delicately, she dipped the tip of her tongue into the wine and moved it over her palate. Then she sipped. "A superior wine. Very pleasant on the tongue, with no bitter aftertaste. A bit fruity, just the way I like it. Do I taste a little cherry and cassis?"

"Yes, as I planned."

"My father used to make a wine with similar ingredients. Oh, I could learn to love this wine. I don't get enough with Pasquale around. He's a man of few words and fewer vices. He agrees with the Vineland philosophy of no liquor stores, no bars."

Like one of the new electric light bulbs, Marcello's face lit up in a smile. They sat alone in the yard, around the picnic table. Marcello continued drinking. "Rosaria, let me tell you how I made it. Winemaking is a very complex process. Chemical reactions, heat, pressure and time all interrelate to make fine wine. And the yeast. It must be superior to make a superior wine. Filtering, adding ingredients, watching, all with the greatest love and devotion. The aging process is most critical. I made the oak casks myself. I spent the last eleven years perfecting this technique, refined from the one my father taught me in Salandra. I'm pleased you like it."

Donata walked into the yard. "We must eat! The food is done, and I don't want it to spoil or go cold. It is a feast in honor of our child's Baptism. Sister, now. Marcello, please, come in and eat."

Marcello took Rosaria's arm. With smiles on their faces, the two made their way into the D'Alessandro's kitchen to enjoy food, homemade wine, and the baptismal rite. They spent the evening in conversation about shared interests.

He invited Rosaria to taste his newest wine at every opportunity.

*

Donata's health declined.

In 1915 Marcello prepared his speech on the birthday of his eldest child. Margharita cooked her own birthday meal and supervised the household chores. The D'Alessandro family sat around the table in their kitchen, odors of dinner lingering. With a flourish, Marcello hoisted his wine—glass for the announcement of Margharita's tenth birthday. "Tonight, you become a woman. Marriage and babies await far in the future. Because of your age, beauty and intelligence, I bestow a blessing on you, Margharita. You will follow your mother and work on our property. Between you, Rocco and your mother we will prosper and have much success. This will allow me to expand our wine business and make superior wine."

Margharita beamed.

Marcello, forced into the decision due to Donata's health, knew the success of the family mandated he take Margharita out of school. Since her pregnancy began, Donata couldn't perform manual labor. After she delivered Virginia later that year, Margharita took over the maternal responsibilities in the fields and at home. Marcello, busy with driving the cart during the day and perfecting the wine at night, spent less time in their home. He left early and returned for lunch, prepared by Margharita before she left for the fields. The children might not see him till ten PM. Life settled into a predictable routine, except for the continuous change in the height of his children.

That decision made, Marcello made another announcement. "Tomorrow is a day off. No work for us."

On November twenty-third 1915, Marcello dressed formally. He sat in the kitchen, finishing breakfast. A slight mist fell outside. He asked Margharita to help Donata get ready for a short trip. She was so weak.

Margharita couldn't understand the change in routine. "Papa, where are you and mother going?"

"You'll see. Everyone is coming. I'll surprise you."

Margharita washed and dressed the children. Minutes later, the family boarded the train to Bridgeton, the County Seat of Cumberland County, New Jersey. Leading a procession of wife and nine children, Marcello marched into gray government building to the door marked "Court of Common Pleas."

His family entered the dark courtroom in silence. No one in the family experienced contact with the law.

As his family took their seats, Marcello asked his two adult male witnesses to sign the documents. Donata managed a smile for her husband as Thomas G. Tuso and Saverio Facovelli signed with a flourish. The men joined the children on long wooden benches and waited.

Judge Le Roy W. Lodis asked Marcello, "Do you renounce King Victor Emmanuelle III of Italy?"

Marcello answered forcefully. "Yes, Your Honor, I do."

The judge went down the row of applicants. They all answered in the affirmative, though renouncing many different kings and countries. "By the power entrusted in me, I declare you are citizens of the United States of America."

The judge signed the naturalization papers. Marcello cried tears of joy as he recited the Pledge of Allegiance. He belonged to the USA now.

The family celebrated with refreshments in the courthouse. They celebrated that night.

The next day he returned to his routine, but Marcello changed. He had a country to call his own. He belonged. Now, he'd act like an American.

After the New Year, Marcello entertained his sister—in—law Rosaria with another wine tasting.

Rosaria enjoyed both the wine and Marcello's company. She trusted her brother-in-law, comfortable enough to divulge family secrets. "Since I gave birth to Maria last month, Pasquale has lost interest in me."

He listened. Everything about Rosaria interested him. "Perhaps he thinks of you. Women need extra rest after giving birth."

"It's been a month. I'm rested. He falls asleep before I come to bed. He's up to work at the glass factory before sunrise every morning."

"Have you spoken with him?"

She shook her head. "Marcello, I don't know what to say. The other women, they don't have this problem with their husbands. What do you suggest?"

Perhaps Pasquale Iurlaro wasn't the right man for her. "Rosaria, cook him a special meal. Pour his wine. Put the children to bed. Let nature take its course."

With the wine finished, Rosaria returned home. Marcello suspected all was not well in Pasquale's house. He put the Iurlaro's out of his mind, climbed the stairs, and looked in on his wife, sleeping in her upstairs bedroom, oblivious to the world. She worsened.

He inspected the house for cleanliness and order. Margharita did all the household chores. She left a covered plate of food on the table for Marcello's dinner.

Marcello sat in the empty kitchen. Donata's health deteriorated daily. Since her pregnancy with Virginia she lay in bed, moaning and praying the rosary, refusing to eat during the day but wandering the house at night, too anxious to sleep. Her body bloated. She developed a cough and difficulty breathing. The malady worsened after the birth. Marcello feared his wife's condition might not improve. Always tired, she never had the strength for work. She hurt all over. Nightmares disturbed her sleep. What was a man to do, if his wife were incapable of fulfilling her marriage vows?

His thoughts turned to the house across the street. Poor Rosaria, frustrated at her husband's lack of attention.

Marcello sighed. He promised Donata there would be no more children. But no physical love?

Marcello lost his appetite.

*

With good weather in the summer of 1916, the Italian community of Vineland spent the evenings outdoors. Marcello built an outdoor fire for the night's dinner and invited Rosaria and her husband. She tied a new scarf around her neck.

"Come quickly! Rosaria, help."

Rosaria heard shouting at her door. Outside, Donata ran towards her house. Perhaps her illness ended. Or was that fear in her voice?

"Something's happened, Rosaria, help me. Quickly." Donata ran back to her home, beckoning her sister to follow.

Rosaria picked up her children Rosa and Maria and followed. A clammy chill ran down her spine.

A single house separated them. Rosaria ran into the sunlight in the back yard of the D'Alessandro's. The late afternoon holiday bonfire roared. Rosaria saw her sister bending over Rosie, her favorite daughter. A moan escaped Donata's lips. Rosie's long, flowing dress disintegrated into black cinders. The child didn't move.

Rosaria stooped and checked the child. Breathing, but slowly. She removed the dress. Black skin where soft, white baby skin used to be. Belly, arms and legs destroyed. The girl looked out with wide eyes, saying nothing. "Donata, what happened?"

"I don't know."

Cinders from the fire soiled the dress and stuck to her skin. Rosaria smelled the charred flesh. The urge to run and vomit struck her. With a prayer to the Almighty, she took Donata inside and gave her the children. "Stay here. Help Rosa and Maria. I'm going to call the ambulance. Just sit here."

"Yes, Rosaria. Help save my Rosie."

Rushing outside, she surveyed the pitiful child. Barely six years old, Rosie lay silent, fighting to breath, eyes wide in a stare. "Where does it hurt, child?"

"Everywhere."

Rosaria phoned the ambulance from her house. She returned with butter, slathering the soft grease on burns of the belly, moved to the arms, and finally the legs. The burnt dress imbedded into her skin. She cooed to the child and brushed her hair.

"It doesn't hurt any more, auntie," the child whispered.

The attendants arrived, bundled Rosie on a stretcher and raced to Millville Hospital, four miles south of Vineland. Rosaria never let go of the child's hand. At the hospital, doctors worked furiously.

Rosie never regained consciousness. She died the next day.

Accidental burning, the death certificate read. The little child played with something she should not touch. Intense flames ignited the little girl's flowing dress. Slow, painful burns and asphyxiation.

Rosaria sat with Marcello and Donata. "The doctors said there was nothing you or they could do. There will be no police inquiry. An unavoidable tragedy. I'm sorry."

The next day Rosaria helped the D'Alessandro family prepare. Marcello cried. He slumped in a pew at the funeral in Sacred Heart Church. Donata sat rigidly, a blank mask on her face, unable to grieve or communicate her feelings. Neither parent could respond to the pleas of the children. They fought their own grief and guilt.

They buried the tiny girl in Sacred Heart Cemetery.

Rosaria did her best. She stroked Donata's forehead and placed a cool cloth. She recruited Rocco, the eldest son, to help with family responsibilities. The boy did his best to be father, mother and brother to the rest of the family.

Rosaria put them to bed that night. Donata fell asleep immediately. Marcello stared at the ceiling. Rosaria left the house shaking her head. Rosie's death changed everything in the D'Alessandro's life.

January of 1917 produced bitter winds and record snow. Marcello's sister-in-law Rosaria visited the hospital in spite of the bitter cold outside. The visitor's area contained several simple chairs and a small table. Quiet and sterile, the old furniture looked worn and abused by thousands of worried relatives of the sick.

Marcello hung his head, exhausted. "Donata does poorly. The doctor says she has catarrh, depression and mitral valve prolapse. She speaks little, eats even less."

Rosaria brought her children with her to Millville General Hospital. Bad dreams of Rosie's death the previous year haunted her footsteps. Pasquale volunteered to stay home and watch the D'Alessandro children during the visit. The train let her off across the street from the hospital. She took her brother-in-law's hand. "What can the doctor do?"

Marcello shook his head.

"Is there treatment?"

Marcello sighed. These family problems sapped his energy. "He's not sure. Her's is a particularly serious case. If Donata doesn't respond by three weeks, he's suggesting a specialist in Philadelphia. The doctor just threw up his hands."

"She hasn't been herself for quite a while, we both know that. Is there any hope?"

"The doctor said to pray."

Rosaria intertwined her fingers in the rosary. "Let me see her. I'll bring her out of this illness. Perhaps it's something only her sister could understand. Perhaps it's a family thing, you know?"

"Do whatever you can, Rosaria. Thank you."

Rosaria completed her rosary in her sister's room. Donata never woke. She left for a break.

Marcello sat in the waiting area. "How is she?"

Rosaira's eyes filled. "She won't speak to me, she doesn't seem to respond. I'm sorry, Marcello, I did my best. I'm unable to bring her out. I don't know what else to do but pray."

Marcello looked into her black eyes. He couldn't think of anyone who understood him like his sister-in-law. "Thank you, Rosaria. I appreciate all the help you have given me during this terrible time. Whatever started this, Rosie's death pushed her over the edge. I feel terrible for her, and for the children."

"You poor man. You are a provider and a leader for your family. Such things should never happen, least of all to you."

He relished the comforting words from Rosaria. He decided to bare his soul. He took her hand between his, glancing about the room. They were alone. "God forgive me for saying this. I feel betrayed. Donata always was quiet. She might have done better with Pasquale, a fine man of modest taste and ambition. But I pushed and insisted on a better life, an easier existence. I like to enjoy life and its pleasures, wine, women, song. You and I might have made a better match, so long ago in Salandra. Then we wouldn't be having this trouble, and me with all the children to raise by myself. My God."

She glanced behind her. No one intruded. "God forgive you, Marcello. You might be right."

The doctor released Donata from Millville General Hospital after three weeks, but she failed to improve. Catarrh, he called it. That and depression. He made arrangements with the specialist, an expert in psychiatry, from Philadelphia.

Marcello sat alone in his kitchen. Medical bills ate at savings for the children, for the family. His wife was the most important thing in his life, above children and country, only eclipsed by God. He thought of Donata's illness.

The cold, dark months of early 1917 brought tragedy. Repeated health catastrophes for Donata. A world war. Mandatory signup with the government, in case America needed more soldiers.

Rosaria provided his only relief. She moved in to the D'Alessandro house, helping with the children, bathing Donata, fixing Marcello's lunch. During the day she cleaned both houses and cooked both dinners. For her sister, Rosaria took on everything.

Rosaria and Marcello shared a glass of their favorite wine together, late in the evening. "She's a good woman, my sister. She produced a fine family and prays to God daily. She deserves a better fate than this."

Marcello nodded. "Yes."

"Donata used to be the happy one, in Salandra. Never a frown. Obedient to our parents, even when they forbade her to marry you."

"Those were tough times. Customs are different in the old country. Here people have freedom."

She took his hand. "I pray to God for you and your family."

Marcello shuddered at her touch. He lost his mind from grief. He reached out and touched her, needing succor. In a mix of fear, shame and passion, he continued.

She responded, urging him on. In the dark recesses of the house, the touch grew into infidelity.

They both demanded more.

The next morning, Marcello's mood changed. Energy flowed through his body. Over breakfast, he took a calculated view of his disastrous family matters. Donata didn't improve. She worsened, withdrawing into her mind, shriveling to a shell of her former vibrant self. To assuage his conscience, he followed the advice of the doctor from Millville General. He dressed his wife and took her to Philadelphia to the specialist.

The physician took one look at Donata that March morning and hospitalized her immediately.

Marcello consented. He had eyes. He saw the change. He knew the outcome now, in advance. He left her at Philadelphia General Hospital, kissed her goodbye, and took the return ferry to Camden. With a heavy heart, he boarded the West Jersey and Seashore electric train back to Vineland. When he relayed the news to the children, the groans and prayers spread throughout the neighborhood.

Marcello felt a deeper loss in the following days. He rued the loss of the one bright star in his life. Without Donata to care for, Rosaria moved back into Pasquale's home. Marcello would care for children all night, work all day. What of his wine?

What of love?

They escaped his grasp.

Marcello settled into his routine as Donata remained under intensive treatment in Philadelphia. Marcello kissed each child in turn before Margharita put them to bed. He walked outside to tinker with the wine.

Drawing a small glass, Marcello sat at the picnic table, head in hands. A sound made him stir. "Who is that?"

Rosaria approached, put her hand on his shoulder.

He took her hands in his. "Donata worsens. The doctor will treat her to the best of his ability. He gave little encouragement. I'm at a loss. I cannot care for eight children, work all day, and maintain my love of life. Thank God He brought you here. You are the only brightness in the day."

She smiled at his comment. "No cure?"

He shook his head.

"No encouragement?"

"Nothing."

"Why?"

"I do not know."

"I'm sorry for you, Marcello." She kissed his head.

"It's not her I think of for these past weeks. You consume me. We are of similar tastes and needs. Think of my wine. I spend hours on tender loving care, nurturing it to perfection. They despise it. You see a new facet of life in it. We belong together to share the fullness of the life God gave us. God forgive me, Rosaria."

After a silence, she sat next to him, placing her head on his shoulder. She moistened her lips. "I feel the same. I have a loving husband, utterly unsuited to pleasing my tastes, my passions. You satisfy my every desire. God will have to forgive us."

Marcello put Donata's illness out of his mind and concentrated on work, children, and family life. He planned for his future. He planned each detail down to the second. Every contingency of weather, transportation, communication, illness or accident. Then he schemed again till nothing remained uncertain.

He would execute his plan, regardless of the consequences.

At lunch, Marcello returned to his home on Cherry Street and sent his seven children outside. For March, it wasn't very cold, and the sun shone brightly. Pasquale stayed busy all day at the glass factory. No one disturbed him.

Marcello sat bolt upright in his kitchen chair, playing with the candle. He waited for Rosaria to finish with her two children and fix his lunch. The bright light filtered through the windows, illuminating the empty table.

She knocked and entered.

"Rosaria, I'm not hungry today."

She glanced around the first floor rooms. "What have you done with the children?"

"I wanted you all to myself. I sent them to the park. They will return in one hour. That should be enough time."

Rosaria busied herself by washing the dishes.

"Rosaria, I want to talk."

"I can't believe you are not hungry. I made some soup, and I brought gnocchi from our house just for you."

"I want you," Marcello whispered. He stared at her neck.

"I don't know what you mean."

He saw her fingers turn white as she gripped the kitchen sink. She trembled.

He walked toward her and touched her back. "I want to live with you. Leave this village with me. We will start a new life. A life we both enjoy, with time to do the things worth doing. Love, passion, dancing, wine. I'll make you happy, not just content. We will rise to the top and be successful, like cream to others milk. I need you."

Rosaria pulled out a chair and sat heavily. She wiped her eyes with her handkerchief.

He touched the soft curve of her neck. "Don't think, feel."

"Not now."

"Listen to me! I planned it all. We will do this together. I will announce Donata is ready to return from the hospital, that she asks you to accompany me. You write a note to Pasquale, say it's from the nurse caring for Donata. It doesn't matter, he can't read anyway. Say it's imperative you pick up your sister. She would be distraught if you didn't."

She stared at the table, not breathing.

"We leave on the train, I've checked the schedules. We head west, keep going till we run out of land."

He glanced at Rosaria. Was she receptive? Or outraged? "We make a life. We love. We die happy. Will you do it?"

Rosaria soaked her handkerchief. "I can't."

He sat next to her. His future depended on her answer. He dared pray to God. "Please, I implore you. We need each other. We deserve each other. You must come with me. I need you."

Rosaria ran her fingers through her hair. "My children, what of my children?"

"Pasquale is a good provider. You said that yourself."

"Do you expect me to abandon them? What kind of a monster would I be?"

"Pasquale will raise them."

"How could anyone love a person like that?"

Marcello stood over her. "I love you. Isn't that all that matters?"

Rosaria walked around the kitchen, pacing as she wrung her hands. "What about my sister?"

He looked into her eyes. "She is dead. If you leave with me, I'll give you as many children as you wish, and the means to support them. I have money to buy what you want, what you deserve. Will you come, so every night will be like last night?"

"Shush. Don't talk like that."

She paced across the tiny kitchen, stopped behind Marcello and put her hand on his shoulder. After a long silence she murmured.

A soft "Yes."

The morning of April fourth 1917 dawned clear and cool. Marcello gathered the children together for a talk. As head of the house, he did not make it a habit to share such information. They sat in silence. "I leave soon to pick up mother at the hospital. Rocco, put the children to bed if I am late returning. Your aunt Rosaria will come with me. Do you understand?"

"Yes, father, I'll do my best."

Marcello handed Rocco a sealed envelope. "Do not open this till tomorrow."

Marcello walked over to the Iurlaro's to speak with Pasquale. He squeezed into their rented apartment. "My wife begs that Rosaria come with me. We are to pick up Donata at the hospital today. It would mean a lot to us both. Can she do that?"

Pasquale respected his brother-in-law. He looked up to Marcello ever since Marcello helped him get settled in Vineland. "Go ahead. But come back tonight because of my two children and your many children. She showed me the note from the nurse. I hope your wife is better."

"All right, we'll be back tonight. Thank you for your kindness, Pasquale." They shook hands like civilized gentlemen.

Marcello left plenty of time to finish his last chore before the nine thirty-eight AM train. Walking from Pasquale's to the bank on Landis Avenue, he pulled on the door handle. The door was locked.

He checked his watch. Almost nine o'clock. The door swung open right on time at nine AM.

Marcello withdrew his savings. "I need to pay a large hospital bill for my wife. She comes home with me today from Philadelphia General Hospital."

The bank clerk smiled and finished the transaction. A fellow Italian, they'd seen each other at Sacred Heart Church. "I will pray for your wife, sir."

Marcello placed the money in a valise. Leaving the bank, he walked down Landis. At the park, starting to turn green after the long winter, he strode to the railroad platform. No one joined him. His gaze searched for her. He waited on the platform, warm from the exertion. Panic overtook his thoughts.

From the east, the sounds of the train approaching reached him. He turned to run.

There. Across the street. "Hurry, Rosaria, or we'll miss the train."

He walked to her, gave her hair a little pat, and took her hand. They waited in silence for the train, slowing near the platform in the pleasant Vineland park.

She trembled and leaned on his arm.

They boarded the nine thirty-eight AM train to Camden. The eyes of the other passengers showed nothing out of the ordinary.

They vanished.

A

CHAPTER NINE

RIPPLES

Vineland, New Jersey, April fifth, 1917. After throwing the pebble, the effects ripple outward, disturbing the pond.

Filomeno Gallo, a kind neighbor near Second and Cherry, checked on the children the night of April fourth. She loved children of all ages. The younger kids stayed at the D'Alessandro home. They played quietly. After helping with dinner, Mrs. Gallo left them to play.

Everything seemed in order when Pasquale Iurlaro returned from the glass factory. He checked the D'Alessandro's house before dinner, allowing the children to stay together till Marcello's return. At eight PM, expecting that Marcello had difficulty transporting his sick wife, he allowed the children to sleep together for the night.

The next morning, Mrs. Gallo heard a commotion and ran to the D'Alessandro's to investigate. Mrs. Gallo found chaos. Entering the house, the D'Alessandro children screamed. "What happened, my children?"

Rocco, between sobs, said, "Mrs. Gallo, we were alone all night." "Why has that let you upset the little ones?"

Rocco bowed his head. He removed the letter left by Marcello and read it to her.

"Dear Rocco,

Take your sisters and brothers and bring them into some home, with the exception of Dominic. Do not put Dominic into a home. I also command you to go to the hospital and get your mother and bring her home. I have gone with Rosario Iurlaro. It is my fault and not Rosario's. She felt very sorry for what she did.

Your father."(10)

Mrs. Gallo cried with them. Then she took charge. Comforting the babies, she then knelt for a prayer. As quiet returned, she left Rocco with the children and sought help. She stopped at Pasquale Iurlaro's place of work, the glass factory. She demanded to see him. The manager led the way. "Mr. Iurlaro, your wife will not return. She is dead."

Pasquale said, "What do you mean by such an outrageous statement?"

"Dead to you. She has gone off with Marcello. They have been unfaithful."

Pasquale sat next to her. Looking into her eyes, he realized the truth. He told the manager and walked her back to the D'Alessandro house. "Thank you for your help. Please stay with the D'Alessandro children."

His children gathered around. He scooped them into his strong arms and kissed them.

He approached Rocco, Donata's oldest. "Son, may I have the letter? It is important."

Waiting for Filomeno to return to watch the children, he calmed them. He couldn't still the beating, while his heart burst. The kind neighbor brought neighbor Rosa Sachetta and volunteered to stay with the children till other arrangements could **be made.**

Mrs. Sachetta told them a soft, beautiful story in her native Italian language. Pasquale, with the stress of the day, left his children under her care.

Pasquale sought Frank DeLuca at his office on Landis Avenue. A prominent Italian attorney and Justice of the Peace, Mr. Deluca dressed in a formal business suit. DeLuca held great respect with the other Italians of the community. He read the letter out loud.

Upon hearing the words, Pasquale asked, "What must I do for justice?"

"Go to the police. Have an arrest warrant issued for D'Alessandro. After that, hire a private detective to find them. Then we must make arrangements for the children."

Pasquale did as he was told. Ashamed to admit his wife left with another man, he nonetheless marched to the police station on Landis Avenue and filed a report. The officer issued the warrant for Marcello's arrest. He then walked across the street to the office of Frank Lore, private detective. Pasquale paid fifty dollars for Mr. Lore to work on the case for three months. Satisfied he did everything possible, Pasquale returned home.

After a sleepless night, banging on the front door awakened Pasquale. The sun barely rose over the horizon.

Rocco stood on the front steps. "Uncle, I must go. I must follow my father's commands and get my mother. May I have your permission?"

Pasquale put his hand on the eighteen year—old's shoulder. "Yes, of course. From now on, son, you are the head of the D'Alessandro house. You may do as you wish. The women will stay until you return."

Rocco took the same train as his father had. Traveling directly to Philadelphia General Hospital, he entered the huge building for the first time. The staff brought him to his mother. He readied her and they left. Rocco couldn't pay the bill. The family had no money.

Donata, weak and listless, could hardly walk. Rocco helped her on the train. She asked few questions. He did everything possible to keep her comfortable. Most of the journey they sat in silence.

When they arrived home, Mrs. Gallo and Rosa Sachetta helped her into bed. Then they told her the reason Rocco picked her up. She took the news calmly. They didn't know if it was her illness or if she expected something like that. Donata asked them to leave. She fell asleep.

The neighbors agreed. Her spirit was destroyed.

Donata rarely left the house. She seldom left her bed. Shrinking to less than ninety pounds, she sat silently by as Margharita raised the babies, Virginia and Elizabeth. Donata thanked Rocco and Margharita for taking good care of her needs. She begged Margharita, *"For the love of God, keep all our children together under one roof, like a real family."*(11)

Donata Onorato, born in the village of Salandra Italy in 1881, died at home on September fifteenth 1917. Burial was at Sacred Heart Cemetery, where she rests next to her favorite daughter Rosie. A gravestone with her name, birth date and day of death marks the grave. Her brothers and neighbors refused to bury her under the name D' Alessandro.

Rocco did as he was told, placing the older children in foster homes. Rocco then left Vineland. He returned many years later.

Margharita stayed on in the house to make a life. She and Rocco were too old to be adopted.

Elizabeth and Virginia, the youngest infants, were placed in the orphanage. Two barren Italian families took them in as their own..

Pasquale Iurlaro received his final divorce by decree of the State of New Jersey on February twenty-eight 1921. Mr. Lore, the detective hired to search for three months, found no trace of the fugitives.

A

PHOTOGRAPHY

1. The Vineland Railroad station where Marcello and Rosaria escaped.

2. The Rotterdam III

3. The Onorato family, Donata and Rosario's family.

4. Marcello's siblings. Giovanni (upper left), Guiseppi (upper right), Mariangela (lower left), Antonia (lower right)

5. San Francisco Nursery for Homeless Children, home to Charles and Josie Andrews for eight years.

6. The Italian branch of the D'Alessandro family. Offspring of Marcello's sister Mariangela.

7. Charles Andrews and his father, Frank (Marcello) at the World's Fair on Treasure Island in San Francisco Bay.

8. U.S.S. Casa Grande, designation LSD-13.

9. The first meeting of the families on the Autostrada with Domenico and Maria Annunziata.

10. The genealogy circle is complete. Janet D'Alessandro, Mariangela Annunziata, Charles Andrews, Luigi Annunziata, Giovani Annunziata, Domenico Annunziata.

Little Park near W. J. Railroad Depot, VINELAND, N. J.

The Onorato's

Gueseppe, Francesca, Rose, Rosantonia Dinnella Onorato
Rocco "Buster"

102

Giovanni Battista

Giuseppe Francesco D'Alessandro

Marcello D'Alessandro

Mariangela D'Alessandro

Antonia D'Alessandro

THE WHITE HOUSE BUILT ON THE DUNE

Orsola Immac, Domenico, Arcangelo, Luigi, Giuseppina'
Giovanni, Annunziata Vincenzo, Margherita, Mariangela.

CHAPTER TEN.

ESCAPE TO SAN FRANCISCO
April sixth 1917.

Marcello's tension rose highest, the excitement most extreme, just before they left Vineland on the nine thirty-eight train to Camden on April fourth. Today exhilaration and not fear coursed through his body.

Marcello planned well. On reaching Camden, they boarded the ferry to Market Street wharf in Philadelphia, docking at eleven AM. He led his beloved Rosaria, still shaking from fright, tension and fatigue, on the trolley to North Philadelphia Station. He bought two tickets for the twelve fifty-two PM Pennsylvania Limited to Chicago. They traveled light, he with the valise and she clutching a small day bag.

They shopped for new clothes in the terminal. It was a changed couple that boarded, hand in hand, taking their seats with an eye to the view. With a new thin white jacket and flowery hat, Rosaria mingled gracefully with other traveling wives. Marcello, wearing a tie to compliment his jacket and shirt, bought a new fedora that he sported at a jaunty angle. The couple smiled and held hands, kissing like newlyweds.

The railroad service excelled. After dinner and several hours to enjoy the view, the couple retired to the sleeper car to start their new life as husband and wife. The powerful steam locomotive lulled them, and dreams propelled them steadily on this eight hundred twenty-two—mile leg of the journey. Marcello said, "Fear no more, my love."

The next morning, after a continental breakfast in the dining car, the train arrived at Chicago's Union Station on time at eight fifty four AM. Marcello, again in the lead, glanced at his train schedule. They approached the ticket counter, avoiding a pair of policemen on rounds in the terminal. "Two for San Francisco."

The man at the ticket counter wasn't busy. He knew everything about every train leaving Chicago. "It's a long trip, sir. The train winds through Omaha, Nebraska and Ogden, Utah. Fortunately, you needn't worry about changing. It's one car all the way through. What did you say your name was, sir?"

"Andrews, Frank Andrews. I'm traveling with my wife Elizabeth. We're on our honeymoon." He smiled and leaned toward the ticket clerk in a friendly and conspiratorial manner. He planned everything, down to borrowing the name of a wealthy landowner from Vineland, an American name for himself and his wife. He knew the natives in Vineland pronounced Andrews much easier than D'Alessandro. The original Mr. Frank Andrews traveled extensively.

Frank Charles Andrews paid the fare and thanked the clerk. The couple stopped for coffee before boarding The Pacific Express at ten forty-five AM. The Chicago, Milwaukee and St. Paul Railroad operated this line jointly with the Union Pacific and Southern Pacific. Three railroads, one thousand seven hundred eighty-six miles, no long layovers, no worries. Frank and Elizabeth cooed at each other, traveling in style. As the train pulled away from Union Station right on time, the lovers watched Chicago pass outside the window.

The next day they left Omaha at twelve forty AM, fast asleep and comfortable. When he stirred, Marcello noted the elevation gained and marveled at the size of the mountain peaks ahead. Closer and closer they approached during the entire next day.

On the forth day of the trip, the train pulled out of Ogden, Utah, in the midst of the Rocky Mountains, on a cool, breezy April eighth 1917. Never before, even in Italy, had Frank or Elizabeth seen such soaring snow covered peaks, or such green flat, verdant valleys. Elizabeth asked about getting out there and starting another farm.

"No, no my dear. With our tastes, we will be better served in a city. More money and opportunity await us in San Francisco. Besides, the winters here are very cold. Look how the thermometer shows only thirty-five degrees. It is too cold outside for my grapevines to flourish. We will enjoy a better life in San Francisco."

Elizabeth slept poorly that night, the gentle rolling of the train cars failing to quiet her mind. San Francisco, famous for its Italian population, wine, and farming, would soon be theirs. She worried about their safety. Rumors of the earthquake of 1906 made her reconsider their destination. She forced the thought out of her mind, preferring to think of all the gold still remaining in the Sierra Nevada Mountains. Perhaps she could afford some gold jewelry.

"Look, Elizabeth, the hills of San Francisco!"

Frank held her hand. They sat in the railroad car, eyes wide to take in the California scenery. This exceeded seeing the Statue of Liberty for the first time. Sharing this thrill and leading her around their new environment made him masculine, powerful, satisfied. "There are many of us Italians here. They say the climate is excellent, not only for people, but also for the grapes. We will grow grapes and have wine and enjoy life like never before. The world opens to us. Look how beautiful, the San Francisco Bay. *Ti amo.*"

Elizabeth needed constant reassurance, which he felt happy to provide. He never felt more thrilled.

The couple acted like newlyweds on a honeymoon, without a care in the world. Tired but excited, they rolled into San Francisco's Southern Pacific Station at nine thirty AM, April ninth. What a grand station, as big and beautiful as Chicago's. The world was their oyster. Unlimited possibilities awaited their arrival. Frank and Elizabeth Andrews knew no one in the world could trace them.

What would San Francisco hold for their new life?

-

A month later, Frank sat outside for lunch with his friend Sam Cuzenza. Frank Andrews, looking relaxed, tanned and comfortable in his new suit of clothes, faced his friend. Frank soaked in all that the North Beach neighborhood possessed: excitement, romance and the possibility of a fortune in wine sales.

Sam Cuzenza lived in the area for years. A trusted acquaintance, Sam sported a new hat to cover his bald pate. A bit smaller than Frank, Sam had the long nose that marked him as a southern Italian. In the warm sunshine of the late May afternoon, they sipped their wine and commented on its heritage, puffing on their new pleasure the cigarette. He offered his advice. "Frank, would you consider Visitacion Valley?"

They took the view outside a North Beach restaurant frequented by many Italians of the district. Frank heard so much about the Napa Valley. He considered moving there and starting a vineyard. All the major growers moved to Napa for the warm summer days, which ripened the grapes, and the early fall fog, which allowed their sugar content to rise. "The wine country is in

Napa. What will I do in Visitacion Valley?"

Sam took a sip. He placed the glass on the tablecloth colored like the flag of Italy. Moving his corpulent frame slightly, he looked into the dark eyes of his friend. His gravelly voice initiated the painful lesson. "Frank, my friend, be realistic. All you and Elizabeth have done since arriving here in California is drink wine, party, and eat at famous Italian restaurants. Don't you want a family?"

"Yes, of course. In due time."

"And a regular job?"

"I have an excellent job."

Sam shook his head. "The strike at the Southern Pacific Line is turning nasty. They plan to break the back of the workers union. That includes you. Consider a safer, more stable job, Frank. Your savings won't last forever, not at the rate you spend money. Go to Napa, you'll realize the price of land. So, you get a loan. Then, you wait ten years for the grapes to mature, another five for the wine to age and suddenly, you're in business. I think those easy money possibilities are over in Napa. Land is too expensive."

Frank stared hard at his friend. Circumstances, financial and otherwise, forced him to clarify the issue. "Would you know of any available jobs, Sam? Much as I hate to think, I may have to continue a day job while I work on the wine at night. Becoming a vintner might take longer than I anticipated. Wine remains my life's ambition."

Sam Cuzenza took another sip of wine, smacking his lips and smiling at a woman across the street. Now he made progress. "Yes, I can help with a job, Frank. But there's more. I have a cousin who lives in the Valley. Housing is cheap, it's a nice, quiet mixed neighborhood good for kids, and the climate is right. Away from all the ocean fog."

"I've noticed how the fog turns summer into winter."

"Visitacion Valley is close in, so you could take the trolley everywhere. Public transportation is more becoming for a gentleman than taking a horse. I don't think these automobiles will be necessary in the city."

"Sam, I'll contact your cousin about Visitacion Valley. Now, how about the jobs? I better look into those first." Frank Andrews sweat under his new shirt. Glorious though his life seemed, his tastes and lifestyle drew his savings down to nothing. His salary at the railroad kept them solvent, but the strike against the railroad might cut that off. He deserved better. Why was life so cruel?

Sam poured another glass from the bottle. He enjoyed other people's wine. "You'll never get ahead with a prolonged strike. I have a friend who works at PG +E, the Pacific Gas and Electric Company. Electricity is spreading everywhere and they need men who aren't afraid of work. Every week, new blocks get electrified. The days of the old gas street-lamps and gas lamps in the home are over. Everything, including our trolley cars, will be electrified. Just wait and see."

Frank paused to look at a cable—operated trolley car passing in the street. Fully loaded, the creaking and groaning caused a commotion as it continued on its journey to the fishing piers along the Bay. "Tell me about wages and benefits."

"A good starting wage, with plenty of room for advancement. Now the benefits, these are very important to a family man. How old are you now Frank, thirty-six? They have a pension plan to keep you happy when you get old. You see, they're unionized, and the workers have clout. So it's a good place to work, not only because it's a reputable, steady job that you can keep forever, but they pay you even after you retire." Sam took another sip of wine and waited.

The silence hung in the air. He hesitated, reluctant to change anything else in his life. This would postpone his dream of winemaking. Frank sipped, finishing his glass. "Give me a name, will you Sam? I think I'll go now, see what's available. It just might work."

"I'm glad I could help." He scribbled the supervisor's name and phone number on a napkin. Another finders fee. This might turn into a full time job for old Sam Cuzenza.

Elizabeth loved Visitacion Valley. She met other women just as eager to gossip and raise a family. Many Italians made their home nearby. She found the neighborhood simple but adequate.

She didn't think of the neighbors today. Foot tapping, playing with her ring, she sat at the kitchen table in her new dress. Minutes dragged by waiting for her lover to return from his job at PG+E. She heard footsteps. "Marcello, guess what?"

He stopped to kiss her, then frowned. He spoke in Italian. "Don't call me that, Elizabeth, unless you want both of us to end up in jail. What are you hiding?"

Elizabeth approached the subject, advising him without provoking a negative response. "I've got to stop drinking so much wine, and I don't want you to be angry. I've put on weight. Did you notice?"

"Not really. You are still beautiful."

She gazed at him. "I've been so tired lately, it's unusual."

"What is it, Elizabeth?"

"The doctor says I'm pregnant."

Frank walked over and kissed her. "Wonderful! Do you feel healthy?"

"I feel fine."

"I hope it's a boy, my little dove. After you make me dinner, we will plan."

She set about cooking, surveying her domain. The move to One Eighty-Four Cora Street in Visitacion Valley pleased her. But she saw little room with a child running about.

Elizabeth pouted. She returned from another trip to the bathroom, joining Frank in the sunlit kitchen. "Frank, are you happy about the baby?"

"Of course, my dear."

"Remember the night, when you said if I ran with you, I could have as many babies as I wanted? This is just the beginning of a large family. Perhaps three boys and two girls."

"Yes, of course I remember my promise. I'm just glad I took the job with PG+E. With more mouths to feed, we'll need the income. Just how do you intend to pick a boy from a girl?"

"God will provide, Frank."

"I hate to say it, but I may have to put the vines on hold for a while, till we see how things are with a new baby. I suppose you will have to quit your job as the pregnancy progresses?"

"I won't quit till the last minute, Frank. I don't agree about giving up your dreams of making wine from your own grapes. Let's save a little each month till we can buy some acres south of here, like the Saratoga vineyards, high up on the Coastal Range. You could grow and press there. It's just a short trip. Doesn't Mondavi work there?"

"Yes." Pouring a glass, he lit his cigarette and leaned back to relax.

"No smoking around the baby, Frank." Elizabeth hustled him outside. None of those nasty habits around the pregnancy.

Elizabeth settled into a new routine, preparing for the baby. She grew by the minute.

The climate in San Francisco wasn't nearly as harsh as in Vineland. No snow to clog the streets, no ice to slip on. Citizens of America rejoiced that the country came through the Great War victorious. She loved her man and kept a house and garden. Everything in her worldview was perfect, save for the terrible influenza epidemic killing thousands of Californians.

Elizabeth Andrews reached the pinnacle of joy with the birth of Josephine in January of 1918. She called her Josie.

Before too many years he would finish the payments and the house would be his. More children would only delay his success.

Peeking out the window, his eyes fell on his vegetable garden. The produce was good, but *Il mio Dio*, he wished for grapevines. He adjusted to the reality of their lives, buying the grapes wholesale and starting the process from there. Without good grapes, Frank feared the end product might not be superior. The quality of wine became a constant source of worry and frustration. Now, another mouth to feed. Another distraction.

Frank bounced Josie on his knee. A pretty girl. He tired when she cried. "Elizabeth, some get the baby. I've got work to do in the yard."

Time flew for Elizabeth, content as a mother could be. The infant Josie sat on her lap, playing quietly. New curtains of lace adorned the living room windows, presents from her neighbors. A new carpet covered the hardwood floor, protecting Josie's attempts to walk. As she fed Josie her pabulum, Elizabeth felt the stirrings of another pregnancy. This time, she wished for a boy, to please Frank. Could life be more perfect?

She spoke out loud for the baby's sake. "Frank works so hard for us, laboring at PG+E all day, working the garden and making wine all evening. If only he didn't smoke so much."

Frank provided for them both. Elizabeth understood he liked the manly routine, and it kept him away from routine household baby chores. She loved everything about babies. Josie was a good baby, easy to care for. Elizabeth knew no greater joy than to birth, care for children, and gossip with the neighboring women.

The knock on the front door startled her. "Inez, come in."

Inez Ferrara, their neighbor on Cora Street, enjoyed children and often visited just to play with the baby. The women shared neighborhood gossip. Sitting behind the lace curtains, Elizabeth waved to Inez on the tiny front porch.

As Inez sat next to her, Elizabeth's mind raced. Where would they put the next baby? Then she thought of Frank, and calmed herself. She'd think of something else to speak of with Inez. "I'm just feeding the baby. How are you today, Inez?"

Thinner than Elizabeth, Inez stood slightly taller, especially in fashionable high heels. She shared dark Mediterranean skin as well as dark hair and eyes. "Fine, thank you. I came to borrow a cup of sugar. I'm making some special bread for my husband. He deserves it, the way he works. Let me feed

Josie for a minute."

Opening the cupboard, Elizabeth poured the sugar. She hummed a popular tune played regularly on the radio. She never could keep a secret from her friend. "Inez, I have some news."

Inez bounced Josie up and down on her knee. "I noticed that smile on your face. Did your husband earn a promotion?"

She shook her head, savoring the moment. "I don't know about that. It's more exciting than work. I'm pregnant again."

Inez jumped up to kiss the new mother. "Wonderful, beautiful. What did Frank say?"

Elizabeth remembered Frank's promise to have lots of children. "I haven't told him yet. I wanted to be sure. It's still early, and I was afraid I might lose him."

"So sure he's a boy?"

"Yes. He feels like a boy, much different from Josie. More activity and motion. Always punching and kicking. You know how much Frank wants a boy."

Inez crossed herself. "*La mia Dio*. I hope he's as happy as you. It's like a sign across your forehead, the happiness. No morning sickness or fatigue?"

"I'm wonderful, Inez. Thanks."

Inez took her hand. "You must rest and take care of your health. A second child is much different from the first. Good luck and God bless. I'll say a rosary for you and the baby. Thanks for the sugar. I must go before the men come home. Congratulations."

A short time later, after the kiss and a small glass of wine, Frank received the news. He stood, felt her belly with his hand. He smiled. "Excellent. And you think it's a boy? Even better. We need a celebration! Tomorrow is Saturday and I have the day off. Let's take a trip to Sausalito. There's something I want to show you. Will your condition allow a short trip?"

The trio arose early the next morning. Frank Andrews always rose by 5:30 AM. Today, his wife got up with him to prepare a picnic basket. They allowed Josie to sleep to the last possible minute.

After a short walk, Frank guided her on board the trolley car, paying a dime fare for both adults. Everyone aboard commented on Josie's looks and offered to hold her. Elizabeth struck up a conversation with a neighbor, and the long ride passed quickly in gossip, sun bathing, and sightseeing.

Frank studied the city. San Francisco looked much bigger than Philadelphia. Around the hill, they entered a more densely populated neighborhood of Victorian homes. The trolley wound through the business district, quiet this weekend morning. As they continued down the hill towards the piers, the smell and sounds of the bay reached him. A very pleasant influence, that bay, and the water looked calm, still and beckoning.

Frank helped Elizabeth off the trolley. They walked across the Embarcadero to the San Francisco Ferry Terminal. Another nickel ferry ticket each, and they sat, hand in hand, waiting for their ride across the Golden Gate. Frank, wearing his hat, woolen jacket and vest to ward off the cool wind, pointed out the area. "Look, Elizabeth. Over to your left. See where the damage from the 1906 earthquake shows? They built on landfill into the Bay, and it is unstable."

Bystanders commented on Elizabeth's fashionable long dress, with a warm hat tied under her chin, and shawl over the shoulders. The baby slept quietly in her arms. "Such a change from New Jersey, Frank."

The steam ferry, a tandem side-wheeler named the *Newark*, arrived. "Wait, Frank, it says Tiburon, not Sausalito."

Walking up the plank, Frank explained. "A little surprise, dear. Something I want to show you. We'll still have our picnic, just in a different area. Don't worry."

The ferry accommodated the passengers with room to spare. The family stretched out while Alcatraz and Angel Island passed by. As the wind and wave action picked up Frank chatted with Elizabeth to ease her concern. The strong sun shone through the glass, warming the baby as they enjoyed the half hour trip.

Disembarking, Frank led them north on the street. "Feel like a little walk? I want to show you something."

"Of course, as long as we walk slowly."

He strode off, carrying the picnic basket on his arm, whistling a tune. They walked past coffee shops and boutiques, well beyond their means. But walking was free, the sea air pleasant, and sun shone to warm them.

Elizabeth played along with the game. Josie fell asleep. The adults enjoyed the touring.

Frank stopped and pointed.

"What, Frank? Hills, water, fishing boats?"

Frank grinned. "Grape vines. See, going up the hill? It's so much closer to home than Saratoga. The Golden Gate shields it from the worst of the cold and wind, and there is plenty of fog for moisture. Wouldn't it be the perfect place for my vineyard?"

Elizabeth breathed heavily as the baby kicked. "Surely. Grand. How much is land here, I hope it's not pricey. Have you checked?"

"Not yet, dear. All in good time."

"Will it get enough sun to ripen the grapes and add to the sugar content? What about the soil, forgive me, but it looks barren."

Frank's smile conquered all protests. His mood soared with the wind on such a fine day, dreaming of the future. "Come, let's have lunch, and perhaps a little nap. Then we can speak to a realtor and walk on the vineyard, my vineyard."

After lunch, Elizabeth and Josie stayed behind.

Frank found a realtor. He followed the man to the hillside, asking question after question. He spoke of his plans for the rest of the day. Then came the complaints about the price of land.

Frank Andrews didn't get another chance to visit Tiburon. Work, household duties, and Elizabeth's pregnancy took up his time. As a compromise, Frank planted one row of ten grape vines in the back yard. He chose Cabernet Sauvignon vines. After studying the angle of the sun, he placed the stakes in strategic locations. In several days of intense activity, he had the vines planted, watered, staked and coiled to rise toward the sun and yield grapes. All in good time.

On November tenth 1919, Frank made an emergency visit to the local physician, Nellie B. Null, MD. "She's in labor. Please, doctor, come quickly. She's at home with the baby. We need your help."

Doctor Null guided the mother through her labor. Charles Frank Andrews, as he was known from the first, birthed without incident. As was the custom, Dr. Null filled out the birth certificate with their legal names, not the common names they used in the neighborhood. In the throes of excitement, Frank dictated the information to Dr. Null.

"*Father- Marcello Dalessandro.*

Mother- Rosa Onorato.

Child- Marcello Dalessandro." (12)

Elizabeth nursed the baby in her bedroom, cleaned from last night's ordeal. Although tired, she felt the joy of bringing a new life into the world. "So big and strong and full of character. Look at those feet. He might grow to be even bigger than you. Isn't he beautiful, Frank?"

To father a son held special meaning for Italians. He reveled in the moment. Dreams for this child sprang unbidden. "Yes, he is beautiful. I'm so proud to have a boy, a big strong boy."

Josie cried in the other room. Frank looked in and smelled the diaper.

"Here, Elizabeth. Let me get her for you."

After placing the twenty-two-month-old Josie on her mother, Frank looked about the tiny room. Where would they live? Men, they didn't need much space. But these women, they were another story.

Elizabeth saw the worry on his face and followed his eye around the room. "Frank, I'm scared. Will our family be all right?"

Frank said, "Everything will be fine, God willing. For Italians, family is everything."

The next day, ahead of schedule, Elizabeth took Charles Frank Andrews to the Catholic Church in Visitacion Valley to be Baptized. A short ceremony, the Latin rite, water on the forehead, and little Charles became a Catholic. His soul was saved. Elizabeth relaxed for the first time since the birth.

A

CHAPTER ELEVEN

DESCENT
Visitation Valley, 1922

Frank's perception didn't lag far behind his friends and neighbors. He noticed the change in Elizabeth after their third child, David, born in 1922. Though their children remained healthy, strong and playful, Elizabeth reacted differently.

Frank enjoyed laborer's work at PG+E. His generous salary helped him secure their finances. They moved to a bigger flat on Cora Street, with two stories, more room and privacy for the adults. Visitacion Valley remained ideal for the children, a small, quiet isolated neighborhood good for families.

Frank sat in the backyard of his new home, tending the grapes. His thoughts darkened as he watched Elizabeth. She acted more subdued than in her earlier years. Perhaps a man could expect that, after three children. They both aged. But Elizabeth's moods changed swiftly. Often quiet and withdrawn, she flew into a rage of shouting, throwing things at him, even cursing. Just as quickly, she reverted into his docile wife. For a year, he didn't think about it. He feared something else, something terrible. He thought about the disease that struck Donata. Did it run in the family?

Frank tried to forget about it, and when he couldn't, explain it away.

Then he ignored it.

Thank God for the children. They enjoyed playing ball with their father, running around and making noise, jumping on him. Frank grew fond of these three kids. It surprised him that mere children could move him so. He took them down to the Bay, showing the boys how to skip rocks off the water, combing Josie's hair till she purred like a cat. When he came home from work, his mood improved as they greeted him, Josie yelling loudly, Charles pulling his hand and craving attention. He loved them.

Inez Ferrara noticed the change in Elizabeth. At first subtle, after several years the clues crystallized. Inez saw a dimming of the bright light of Elizabeth's spirit as she turned thirty. She lost the verve, flair and love of life that attract people like Mrs. Ferrara to those like Elizabeth. Her friends wanted that energy. Now her light started to dim.

Inez Ferrara steeled for the unpleasant task. She knocked on the Andrews door on a fine San Francisco day. She entered the front door into the spacious living room. Its green color made the living room Inez's favorite in the house. She saw Frank pruning in the back yard. Inez knew the smallest things could irritate the man of the house, especially during the hustle and bustle of the holiday season. "Mr. Andrews, you know how my husband Ted likes my bread. Is it too much of a disruption to borrow a cup of sugar from Elizabeth?"

He rumbled around the kitchen, opening and slamming the cabinets. "Hello, Inez, come in. She's shopping, but it's no bother. Let me see if I can find where she keeps it. It must be around here somewhere. How are you and Ted?"

She forced herself to remain calm. "We're fine, thank you. Don't exert yourself, Mr. Andrews. I know where it is. I'm always misplacing things around the house. Does Liz misplace things besides sugar?"

Frank turned to face his guest. He stood at the entrance to the kitchen, one hand behind his back, the other clutching a cigarette he rolled by hand. Frank threw open the sash and breathed deeply. "I work all day, and I seldom cook. I wouldn't know about kitchen utensils. Why do you ask?"

Inez walked towards the door. Perhaps she had miscalculated, or misinterpreted the situation. Either way it was none of her business. "Oh, sorry I asked. Probably I worry too much."

He whispered. "She's forgetful."

Inez knew this information bode ill. But Elizabeth's behavior wasn't right. They faced each other across the table. She hesitated. "She's not her old self. Sometimes she sits in the chair in the front room for hours. The curtains stay drawn, even on the warmest days. The children play, walk in the street and around the block, and yell at her. After a while she stirs and asks if they want to eat. Then back to the chair. Something's not right."

"I attributed her lack of interest to fatigue, you know, from the children. They are a handful of trouble at times."

Inez wiped her hands on a towel. "She always used to visit me, gossip and drink tea. She hasn't come to my house in six months."

"It's not just fatigue, though. Her mind, …it wanders. She speaks much more of the old country. Nothing about our family or others around us. She doesn't mention you. A definite change. I don't know what happened. I don't know what to do." Frank puffed on his cigarette, shuffled his feet.

Frank's reaction confirmed her fears. She knew there was a problem. She hadn't a clue what caused it. Something in the family, or one of those unspeakable things that happened behind the closed doors of a marriage? "She could have a checkup, a test, to see if there are any problems. I know Dr. Null does such a thing in her office."

Frank took a long drag. "I'll consider it. I'll have to see. Inez, you are a good neighbor."

"I'll let myself out, Mr. Andrews. I hope I didn't disturb you." Inez left the unused sugar on the counter.

Frank sat on the front porch. Yes, they argued. Didn't every couple? But her health, that was important to them both. A visit to the doctor might avert a tragedy.

Elizabeth returned, found her husband sitting on the porch, rocking and smoking another cigarette. She smiled, empty handed, and sat next to him.

"Inez came over for a cup of sugar."

"Oh, she's always baking. Did you give it to her?"

Frank nodded. "Where are your packages?"

She rubbed her hands. "I… what packages?"

Frank's voice rose. "You went shopping. Did you forget?"

Elizabeth's smile lit up her face. "No, Frank, of course not. I left them at the store. It's such a beautiful day, I wanted to take a walk. Will you come back with me and pick them up?"

The first week of December, 1925 the Andrews sat in Doctor Null's office. They looked at each other and held hands, never having visited a physician before save for delivering babies. They sat quietly till the receptionist ushered them into the doctor's office.

Antiseptic odors assaulted their noses. Medical equipment, a microscope, and rows of pills lay neatly arranged on the wooden counter. The doctor entered.

Doctor Null got directly to the point. She wore her white medical coat, buttons open to accommodate her belly, and twirled her stethoscope. Piles of paper lay haphazardly on her desk. She frowned. "How can I help you?"

The doctor could ask questions, and he would answer. That was her job. Frank shifted in the wooden seat. A woman's place...wasn't in a doctor's office. The only doctors he'd met were the male doctors on Ellis Island. "I am concerned about my wife Elizabeth."

Dr. Null looked at the couple across the desk. She hesitated, staring at her books and medical devices behind them. "Perhaps I can help. What seems to be the cause for concern?"

Frank took a deep breath and closed his eyes. "Her memory..."

"Now, Marcello, we both know there is nothing wrong with my memory," Elizabeth said. "I'm just tired from caring for three young ones."

Dr. Null noted the effect on Frank Andrews. "Mrs. Andrews, you just called your husband Marcello."

Frank's words came rapidly, breaking through the pent-up dam. What must the doctor be thinking? "Dr. Null, that's not all. She doesn't sleep, hardly eats, and she's not as interested in life as she used to be. She never gossips with the neighbors. That used to be her favorite past time. Her behavior worries me. Recently she went to the grocers and forgot to bring home the food. I'm worried she maybe is ill."

"Are you two getting along all right? Is there strain in the marriage? Having children is difficult."

"No, not difficult having children," Elizabeth said.

Dr. Null listened.

"Losing them is difficult. My other children, I miss them. Since April, the month we left, I have nightmares. I feel guilty. I can't get them out of my mind. That's why I forget. I'm thinking about something else. Don't worry, I'll be fine. Come on, Frank, I'll get better. Let's go home."

Doctor Null took her glasses off and wiped them clean. "I'm sorry, I didn't know about other children. What happened?"

Frank said, "a long time ago, in another life, she had a baby. Many children died in those days. Almost any illness caused them to go. This one she speaks of seems to have made a lasting impression. I just want you to check my wife, doctor. See if she has a disease. See if you can give her some pills. I need her to care for the children."

The color drained from Elizabeth's cheeks. "The short days makes it worse. At night, the dreams seem real. During the day I can tell it's just my imagination. I'm very frightened at night."

Frank held his head in his hands. "Please check her, doctor. See if she needs some pills?"

With Frank observing and Elizabeth humming, the doctor proceeded with her examination. She stuck the patient's finger and checked the blood count. She asked questions to check memory.

"To answer your question, Mr. Andrews, I can't find anything like pregnancy or diabetes to explain your wife's behavior. No pills will help this. It may be…"

"Thank you very much for your time, doctor," Frank said. "You put my mind at ease. Now we can go and resume our normal life. She'll be fine. Thank you. Please, how much money do I owe?"

After paying the bill, Frank walked Elizabeth home, arm in arm. He spoke in Italian. "Don't ever say those things again, Elizabeth. We keep that secret to stay out of jail. Keep your mouth shut, honey, everything will be fine."

"Frank, you're hurting my arm."

Elizabeth looked into his eyes. "I'm sorry, Frank. I forgot. I won't do it again. Please let go my arm."

Frank made the Christmas arrangements. The family stayed home, and the children enjoyed ripping and opening the boxes. They didn't visit or socialize, but spent time in Church. No one suspected anything amiss in the Andrews home, save for the parish priest who heard Elizabeth's confession.

Life settled into it's normal routine at the Andrews house. On February second, 1926 Frank left for work at PG+E. The children played till noon. Elizabeth asked Josie to take the kids to the park and let their mother rest. She didn't feel well.

"But it's raining, momma."

"Please, Josie. Take them."

When Frank came home for dinner, he found her lying in bed sleeping. "Where is my dinner?"

"I'm sorry, Frank."

"What have you been doing all day?"

Startled, she felt at a loss for words. She stood her ground. "I think I caught the flu. You know Inez had it last week. I didn't feel well and fell asleep. Let me make your dinner."

"I can't believe you slept the day away," Frank grumbled.

"I didn't sleep the day away. I've been thinking about our children. They don't know about us. They don't even know about the others we left behind. It's not right, and it's eating me up inside. I've been to confession, and the

Father thinks I should tell the children who we are and what we did, so we can pray for forgiveness to God Almighty as a family."

Frank raised his voice, bent over and got in her face. "Damn you. I forbid you to tell your pitiful story to the children. I don't want you using this as an excuse to stop working and caring for the family. Look at me, hungry and waiting for dinner, and you feeling sorry for yourself."

"But the priest said God forgives all."

"Get up. Forget what the priest said."

Inez knocked on the front door. "I heard a noise…"

Frank yelled outside. "It's all right, go home. I just want dinner for myself and the kids. Elizabeth thinks she has the flu."

Dinner was late, which put Frank into a worse mood. Elizabeth put the children to bed, kissing each one tenderly. Young David fell asleep. She asked Josie to collect Charles after school the next day and play in the park until their father came home.

She kissed them again the next morning, before breakfast. Frank slammed the door on his way to work. He was in one of his angry moods. Josie and Charles left for school. David stayed with her, playing inside the house. He was too young for school.

After putting little David down for his mid-day nap, Elizabeth said a prayer. With a burst of newfound energy, she went into the kitchen, opened the cupboard, and took out the new bottle of Lysol she bought the week before at the grocers. She cleaned the kitchen till it glistened. No spots remained. Frank would be pleased. He loved a tidy house.

Fatigue returned and she paced listlessly into the bedroom. Sitting on her bed, Elizabeth crossed herself and stared at the statue of the Virgin. She prayed for hours, first the rosary and then prayers from her childhood. Begging for forgiveness for herself and Marcello, she beseeched the Blessed Mother to care for her babies. How she summoned the strength to walk to the kitchen she didn't comprehend.

She forced herself to drink the full bottle of Lysol.

At five thirty PM, Elizabeth walked to the front steps and sat down, limply waving to passers-by. David cried upstairs, alone.

Josie, walking home after collecting Charles from school, saw her and screamed. She crossed the street to Mrs. Ferrara's house.

"Child, what is wrong?"

"My momma is sick."

Her screams came in long, mournful gasps. Mrs. Ferrara clutched the child and tried to calm her. It was fruitless. She wouldn't be consoled. Inez

Ferrara called the ambulance.

Elizabeth fell down, motionless.

Minutes later, Frank heard Josie's scream. He joined them on the sidewalk. "Josie, what are you doing? You should be helping your mother fix my dinner."

"But look, its mother. She must be ill." Josie's little voice wailed.

Frank spotted the prone body of his wife. "Inez, please fetch David and Charles. I will take care of mother."

He ran up to the porch. He sensed the disaster. He saw her lying motionless. Lifting Elizabeth into his arms, he put her in bed. Her unnatural quiet disturbed him. "Elizabeth, Elizabeth, what have you done?"

Inez entered with the children.

Josie's scream brought him back to reality. Holding the bottle of Lysol, Josie walked in.

Elizabeth clutched her belly in the fetal position. The rosary intertwined in her fingers. Drool spilt from her mouth.

"I must call the ambulance," Frank yelled to Inez. "Take the children to your home and stay there till I return."

"I've called the ambulance already."

She died at the Mission Emergency Hospital in San Francisco. Doctor Dalles signed the death certificate. Elizabeth Andrews, as she was known, or Rosaria Onorato, the name inscribed on her headstone, died without responding. February third 1926, at the age of thirty-six years, death by her own hand. Lysol poisoning.

She abandoned Josie, just turned eight, Charles Frank, seven years, and David, all of four years.

She betrayed Frank Andrews for the last time.

At the funeral, Josie cried uncontrollably.

Frank watched as they carried the casket up the steep stairs. "What is wrong, my child?"

"Tell them to be careful. Don't let momma fall."

A

CHAPTER TWELVE

GREAT DEPRESSION

February, 1926. Cora Street, Visitacion Valley.

Frank sat in the living room at Cora Street. The funeral over, only Sam Cuzenza remained.

Frank never did like the neighbors, those busybodies. Thank God for his friend Sam, always able to help in an emergency. Without Sam, he didn't know what he'd do. They put the children to bed. Frank poured two glasses of wine. "I feel abandoned."

Sam nodded. "Yes, sometimes the Lord works in strange ways."

"She abandoned me. Elizabeth never mentioned a word, then took her life. Now I must raise the children."

Sam sipped his wine. Moments passed before he spoke. "Let us plan for the future of those children."

The kitchen bulb threw its dim light. "She left me alone. I don't know what to do."

Sam sipped the wine. "Think about a home. It's best for your children. You can't stop working. With your important job at PG+E, you are busy all week long. Who will care for them every day?"

"I must work. I can't stay at home all day. We'd have no income."

"I looked into it for you. I asked the social worker at the elementary school, Miss Friedman. The best choice is the San Francisco Nursery for Homeless Children. They care for many young ones. It's at Lake and Fourteenth Street, a short trolley ride. You can visit them every weekend and holiday if you like. They help, but they don't take the children away. Sundays they have a Presbyterian Church nearby, during the week the kids attend public school. Have you heard of their reputation?"

Frank shook his head. "David's too small. He needs full time parents. Perhaps Inez and her husband? They don't have any children."

Sam shook his head. "No, it's too close. He'd look out the window and see you. Let me see if there is someone else out of the immediate neighborhood. Please, it's best for the children."

Sam Cuzenza left after midnight, nothing resolved. No decisions made.

Frank pondered his options, rolling cigarette after cigarette and sipping home made wine for comfort during the cool, dark night. Alternatives seemed limited. He needed to work. The children were too young to work or stay home alone. Bringing in outside help remained outside his financial means. Besides, he didn't like strangers in his home. They might steal everything, or worse drink all his wine and not do their job. Frank could not see himself staying home, caring for three children. Full time father, or full time head of household and worker, and let the children go to others.

The San Francisco Nursery for Homeless Children stuck in Frank's head. He heard of it, but where?

Sipping his wine, the answer came. Yes, the 1922 pencil drive. The Nursery, a secular institution with a charter from the city, specialized in helping orphaned and poor children during their time of need. They never refused a child. He remembered the 1922 newspaper and radio publicizing the Home to San Franciscans. Volunteers sold pencils for a nickel. Frank remembered buying one. During raffles and auctions for the rich, they raised thousands more. One pencil brought in $2,000, after a matron bid up the price then gave it to the auctioneer to sell again. Children from the orphanage had the day off, May second 1922. The children flooded the Ferry Building on the Embarcadero. They begged the commuters from the railroad and ferry. "Please, just five cents. Please."

After paying his five cents, one gentleman said *keep the change*. The entire City echoed the cry. *Keep the change*. Children got quarters and dollars for a single pencil. They sold thousands. The total take for the day came to $32,117.29. Frank knew the Nursery for Homeless Children had the resources to care for his children.

*

Sleep wouldn't come that night. Marcello heard the screams.

Frank awoke sweating the early morning after the funeral, February sixth

1926. He couldn't sleep in her bed. Her smell lingered on the pillow.

Sleep wouldn't come, only nightmares. Shuffling to the kitchen he anointed hands, lips, neck and chest with cool water. Strange, to be sweating so much in the cool air. His tank top undershirt usually kept him comfortable. Sitting at the barren kitchen table in the lifeless house, he rolled a tight cigarette from loose tobacco and papers. Inspecting the finished product in the coarse light of a bare electric bulb, he lit the end and inhaled deeply. His mind relaxed. As he puffed, his thoughts drifted with the smoke from the cigarette. The past flashed through his mind. What of the other children?

What happened to them?

He sat up, startled, shirt soaked in sweat. Disoriented, he blinked his eyes and smoked. His dream returned in vivid detail. The cries from his home weren't only this trio of children. He'd heard shrieks and agony of those left behind in Vineland.

After breakfast, Frank cleared his throat. Tired and irritable, he knew he couldn't put off the decision. He must inform the little ones. "Children, we must have a family talk. When I was in Italy, my father always said these words before an important discussion."

Josie, Charles and David finished their eggs and bacon. They slumped, sitting still at the table.

"It is very hard. Your mother is dead. She is gone forever to heaven, and won't return to us. I grieve terribly for her, as I know you do."

David and Josie cried. Charles, rather than cry, bit his lip and hit the wall with his fist, anything to keep from upsetting his father.

Frank tried again. He must not give up, must not give in to despair. "Mother is gone. We are still a family, and I must do what is best for you children. I must continue my job, for money and food and to pay for this house. It is for you I do this. In our culture, family is everything. Not like those born here in America. They don't think anything of family any more."

The plaintive faces of his children tore his heart. Their large brown eyes stared straight through him. They listened and waited, too numb to understand what he planned. If there was any other way. "What will I do with you all day, when I work? You are so young. Josie, I wish you were a little older. You could stay home and care for us all."

Josie wiped her tears. "I can do that. Momma taught me how."

Frank patted her head. "Maybe later when you grow up, you can do that. I have made a decision, based on what is best for you children and our family. Josie and Charles, I will take you to the San Francisco Nursery for Homeless Children. It is a wonderful school where you sleep overnight. They will teach you, feed you and clothe you during the week. It is a very nice place, filled with fun things for youngsters. They will treat you with respect."

Josie wailed. "I don't want to leave home."

Frank cooed. "Don't worry. Every weekend, I will take the trolley and pick you up. We will spend weekends together, as a family. It will be just as it always was. A family, together, caring for each other."

Stifled sobs filled the air.

Frank paused to take a sip of wine. His throat scratched. He couldn't swallow. Looking around the tiny kitchen, everything reminded him of Rosaria, his dead Elizabeth. He heard her soft Italian voice, humming a tune. The smell of fresh baked bread, her favorite. Josie pulling at her apron strings. "David is too little. He will stay with a nice Italian family in Excelsior, towards the Bay. The Ferigaro's have a little horse, a Shetland pony. David can ride the pony every day. When David is bigger, he can join us. David, you won't remember any of this as you get older. You are the lucky one."

Josie cried. Her lip trembled. She pleaded with her father, the master of her small universe. "Please, don't send me."

"You must go to school and grow and be strong. It won't be long and we'll be together again." He rubbed his head to remove the pain of the voices inside.

Josie cried again. Her brothers joined in.

Frank poured himself a small glass. He didn't look forward to the trip. He needed to prepare. It was imperative the children understand his decision.

Charles looked ahead to practical considerations. "Father, what must we pack?"

"Bring all your clothes," Frank commanded. "We will take the next trolley."

Sobbing steadily, Josie packed for herself and David. The family walked to the trolley station. After three stops, they got off, and Frank delivered little David to the waiting Ferigaro's, a young couple with several girls. He kissed his youngest son goodbye, not knowing when he'd see and hold him again. He joined the other children.

Charles and Josie sat in the trolley, Frank standing close by. In the bright morning sun, they rode down Lake Avenue to the San Francisco Nursery for Homeless Children. Soon, the trolley entered the white fog bank bordering the Pacific Ocean. Gloom enveloped them, silent and cold. Frank smelled their fear.

The family exited the trolley and walked four blocks to the corner of Fourteenth and Lake. Josie, we have an appointment. Keep up with us."

Frank pointed out the neat sign on the wall in front. Beyond, he admired the spotless sturdy architecture of The San Francisco Nursery for Homeless Children. The tall, white three—story building dominated the neighborhood. Large windows let in sunlight and the ocean breeze. Thick green hedges separated it from the street. Frank pointed to the boys' quarters on the left of the third floor, and the girls' dorm to the right. A wide, long wooden staircase led up to the dorms. "This is now your home. It is not your real home. Your real home remains on Cora Street. God willing, we will gather there when you are old enough. For now, obey your elders. I'll see you every weekend."

After introducing the kids to the staff, Frank spent hours signing papers, listening to the orientation and rules, and paying the fee. He paid sixty dollars of his total monthly pay of one hundred dollars. He walked his children arm in arm to their rooms and helped them unpack their belongings. Small talk came hard.

After a silence he rose. "I must go, children. Give your father a kiss. I will come back to pick you up every weekend."

The look on their faces broke his heart.

Each morning at six AM Charles and Josie woke, brushed teeth, combed hair and made beds. Then downstairs to the kitchen for breakfast. Soon they walked to the Sutro public elementary school. After lessons came kitchen and cleaning duty. Then dinner.

The only break in the regimen came after the dinner dishes were removed and cleaned. A kindly citizen might leave gallons of ice cream or sheets of cake. The scramble for seconds excited all the children. Then came quiet reading time. Charles and Josie learned the strict study hall and homework routine. The staff inculcated strong work habits into their charges. Finally, early to bed and early to rise. Lights out, when no sound was tolerated. The children grew used to the schedule

Children adapt, blessed with the resilience of youth. The routine at the San Francisco Nursery for Homeless Children kept their young minds from idleness and despair.

On October twenty-ninth 1929, panic selling on the New York Stock Exchange caused stock prices to decline by fifteen billion dollars in a single day. Brokers jumped from the windows of the Exchange on to Wall Street. The streets ran with blood, fueled by panic. Common people as well as brokers lost everything bet on margin and speculation.

Speculation, often on margin buying of three percent of the total price, drove up prices for months before Black Tuesday, fueling the post Great War economic boom. In the first six months of the Hoover Administration, stock prices peaked. Over-extension of credit coupled with a loss of confidence resulted in the precipitous crash. By mid-November, the decline in stock prices totaled over thirty billion dollars. Factories closed. People lost their fortunes overnight. Millions lost their jobs. The economy contracted. The Great Depression began with a bang.

The whimpers of the poor marked their suffering.

-

Frank spoke to the children the weekend before Thanksgiving, 1929. After work on Friday, he took the trolley along the cool, windy Lake Avenue to the Nursery. He found two expectant faces waiting near the entrance. He hugged them, and tears came to his eyes. "Children, come, a kiss. Let's go home for the weekend."

Holding their hands, Charles on the right, Josie on the left, they walked to the trolley station. Frank realized the impact of the stock market crash. The trolley, usually full on Friday evening, traveled half- empty. In the gathering dusk, they journeyed home. "Josie, you are so grown up for eleven years."

"My teachers let me care for the other little ones."

"Charles, did you enjoy your birthday last week?"

"Yes, I got a second helping of ice cream."

"I want to know what they are teaching you. Did you hear about the stock market crash?"

"Of course, father. People jumped out of windows in New York. They lost everything." The diminutive Josie seemed back to her usual talkative self.

"Yes, I heard the same thing," Frank said, "although I find it hard to believe. They still have families, children, and responsibilities. Many lost their jobs."

Josie asked, "What about your job, father?"

"I still have my job with PG+E. Some were let go, but I worked for them for many years. If they let me go the electricity might stop flowing."

The children laughed. They looked at bright electric lights illuminated the neighborhoods.

"I will be working less hours at PG+E. I have taken an extra job building the telephone cable across the Bay to Oakland. Money is very tight. A simple thing like this nickel trolley might become extravagant. This summer I'm going to double the space for our backyard garden. We will eat more vegetables. Soon, I'll let you have a little wine with your meals. There's plenty of that. So, even though I might not see you as often as before, we'll be doing things together."

Josie said, "I don't want to stay at school on weekends. I want to come home."

Frank nodded. "Any time I can afford the trip I will bring you home. The first thing, I'll teach you both to fish in the Bay."

"I don't want to fish. They're slimy," Josie said.

"Then Charles and I will fish. Josie, I'll teach you to prepare the fish after we catch them." As they arrived at their stop near Cora Street, Frank pulled a paper bag from his pocket and showed them the fishing poles he made by hand, with sections of fine line tied together.

After the meal Frank walked the children down to the San Francisco Bay. The setting sun framed fog near the Golden Gate area. The water lay cool and still. "A perfect time to fish, they bite better at dawn and dusk," he told Charles. He demonstrated the technique of casting. "Here, son. Now you try it."

"I got one. What do I do?"

"You catch on fast, Charles," Frank said. "Be careful. Pull slowly, and keep a little tension on the line. Good."

Charlie pulled up the small bass.

"Enough for tonight. Let's go home and try again tomorrow morning. If that works out, some day I'll take you to the ocean and we'll try and catch abalone. It's very different and exciting. I love the taste of abalone."

Josie spotted a man pushing a heavy cart. People sold apples and pencils and other items on street corners. She had conversations with these vendors when she walked to the store. "His cart is full of metal. What is he doing?"

"He's collecting scrap metal. He probably lost his regular job. With the economy in depression, metal is scarce. People pay him by weight, so the more he can push, the more he makes. They use it to make new machines. Its less expensive than buying it new."

Charles looked long and hard at the man. "Father, I could do that. I know a fellow who pays for scrap metal. I could earn extra money so you could take the trolley to see us more often."

Wiping the tears from his eyes, Frank couldn't respond for a moment. "Yes, that is good. You make extra money with the scrap metal. But you may keep what you earn. My advice is to save it for a rainy day. And think about a paper route. It's steady work and you could do it on a bicycle. Son, I'm so glad you understand the value of money. You will do well in life to remember that lesson."

The next morning, while Josie fixed breakfast, father and son fished for an hour a dawn. Frank helped Charles catch and land another fish. "Congratulations, son. Your fish are tonight's dinner. Let's hurry home and I'll teach Josie how to clean this so it won't go bad. You can use the rest of the day to start your scrap metal business."

Charles followed his father's advice. He sat down and thought out the process. Where the metal was, how to procure it, how to transport it. After his research, he walked down Visitacion Valley to the man buying scrap. After striking up a conversation, the man, impressed by Charles's industriousness, agreed to a penny more a pound than he usually gave. Charles built a cart with wheels to haul the metal.

After a business plan and infrastructure he initiated production. The day flew by. Soon, it was dinnertime. Charles, bursting at the seams, couldn't contain himself. "Father, look what I did today."

They sat, the three survivors, at the dinner table on Cora Street. The children said Grace before the meal of fresh fish. Frank saw his squirming son. "Yes, yes, son, what did you do?"

Charles pulled thirty cents in change from his pocket. "I started my scrap metal business. I made a fortune today. No overhead, no expenses, and a good deal from the scrap man. It's all profit."

Frank played with his fish. "Congratulations, son. It looks like you have a feel for business. Keep up the good work. We'll need help to make it through the hard times."

"It makes me feel good to have some money in my pocket."

The next morning, Sunday, Frank understood Josie's prayer. She prayed to stay home.

Charles fidgeted, ready to leave.

Frank's thoughts turned to himself. A lifelong Catholic, he didn't mind missing Sunday Mass or the Holy Days of Obligation. He didn't believe a kindly God would watch over him and love him, even less than he believed in the promise of eternal life. No conversation punctuated their meal.

After supper they returned to the San Francisco Nursery for Homeless Children. Charles went about his duties of cleaning the cafeteria. Josie, still crying, took up her knitting and darning in earnest. Life for the children didn't change in the orphanage. Most of the time they felt privileged. The older boys said their schoolmates who lived at home were the handicapped.

The economic depression continued, unchanged, save for Charles' and others efforts to stimulate the economy. He bought a bike and started a paper route at five AM every weekday morning. Frank said, "Where there's a will there's a way," and Charles had the will.

Josie graduated to Portola junior high school as the children started their sixth year in the orphanage. Charlie continued at Sutro Elementary. Both enjoyed the vigorous routine, summer camp on the river, and camaraderie of their friends and fellow inmates. They grew used to their life.

The depression deepened, despite the efforts of President Roosevelt. Weekend routines changed for the Andrews family. The children stayed at the Nursery Friday and Saturday nights. After Sunday services at the Sutro Presbyterian Church, the children went to their usual Sunday lessons. Few Catholics lived at the San Francisco Nursery for Homeless Children, so they attended the Presbyterian school.

The headmaster of this class, a volunteer Presbyterian lay volunteer uncomfortable with children, had a strict reputation. No foolishness, no fooling around. The lay volunteer strode into the class. "Charles Frank Andrews, please come to the front of the room."

Charles did as he was told. He sauntered up and stood to the side of his teacher. "Children, listen closely. Young Mr. Andrews here receives a special honor today. He has not missed a single session of Sunday school for six years. He is the student enrolled for the longest duration in our history. Let this be a good example for all of you. If you are serious about your faith, attend every Sunday, like young Mr. Andrews. It will make you strong and serve you well as you grow into adults."

"Thank you, sir."

He pinned the award to Charles's shirt.

School let out, and the children ran to meet their father. By now, Charles approached Frank's height. He stuck out his chest. "Father, look at my pin."

Frank met them outside the gate of the orphanage, eager for Sunday dinner. Food was never far from his mind. "Yes, son, what is it for?"

"My endurance," Charles replied. "I've been in Sunday School longer than anyone. Isn't it great?"

"Wonderful. You must understand the Presbyterians. Let's hurry, children. Get on the trolley. I've started dinner and I'm getting hungry." He took their hands and walked. Frank's tone brooked no opposition. When he got hungry, the rest of the world stopped.

They entered their home, cheerful and hungry. Josie set the table. Charles filled the water glasses. The children didn't notice threadbare furniture or peeling paint. A dark tablecloth covered the old table, upon which Josie placed napkins, utensils, and plates. Pictures of the children and of San Francisco sites adorned the walls. Meals were different here. Unlike the San Francisco Nursery, they said no prayer or benediction before tearing into the food. "Josie, prepare the roast."

She brought the food to the table.

"Here you are, children. Good appetite."

"Thank you, father."

"Mind your manners, Josie. Use your fork. Elbows off the table. Sit up straight. I hope you enjoy the food, it costs a fortune, and on my salary I don't have much left after paying your bills at the Nursery."

After cleaning and stacking the dishes, Frank walked them to the nearest trolley station. "Josie, you remember where to transfer? Good, don't get lost. See you children next week."

The children kissed their father.

Paying the nickel fare, he waved goodbye, turned and left them. He had work to do, and a smoke and drink of wine. He needed a little relaxation before the rigors of the workweek started Monday morning.

In January 1933, on Josie's fifteenth birthday, Frank made a visit to the San Francisco Nursery for Homeless Children. He smiled, knowing the children would be pleased. "Good morning. Happy birthday, Josie."

"Yes. I'm fifteen today."

"Josie, I have a surprise for you."

She jumped and screamed. "Tell me. Tell me!"

"You are old enough, Josie. You can come home and take care of the house. We will live together as a family. I can feel at ease about the weekdays when I work. You and Charles and little David will go to school near home, and you can cook dinner for us. Today is your last day here. Children, say goodbye to everyone. We won't be back."

Josie and Charles kissed the staff farewell. After seven years, they left their friends. Favorite teachers who made a comfortable home for them in the midst of hundreds of other children gave them hugs. Now they would live in their real home.

After the tearful departure, the family boarded the Lake Avenue trolley. Frank counted the half month's refund for tuition.

The kids dared not look back.

They made one stop to pick up David along the way. With each passing minute, Josie and Charlie smiled and became more talkative. Soon, the trio of children walked in to One Eighty-Six Cora Street and placed their bags down. Charlie and Josie smiled and yelled and didn't know what to do.

Josie received the private bedroom. Charles and David shared a bed. They each took a private place to store their clothes and mementoes.

Frank apportioned the work. "Josie, cook the dinner tonight. Tomorrow, Charles will fish and we will have that for dinner. Do you remember how I taught you to clean and prepare it?"

"Yes, father. I've been practicing at the Nursery."

"I like it that way, so don't change anything. Welcome home, my daughter. Do your job well."

Josie took over the household chores. Cooking, cleaning and shopping filled her life. School became a blessed change of routine during the day. Her father warned her not to spend too much time on the books. Her primary job remained caring for the men. Books were a waste of time.

Josie continued to hold down the household chores during her second year of high school. To escape the routine of their home and the reprimands of her father, she surreptitiously dated. Though Frank strictly forbade dating, it was her secret. She begged Charlie to keep it that way.

Soon Josie entered a serious relationship. Benny came from a troubled family, yet held down a job as an apprentice sheet metal worker. Warned several times by police, he'd avoided arrest. The couple shared common interests. The dates turned into an alliance against their present situation. They saw each other at every opportunity.

Benny approached her one evening wringing his hands. He shuffled around and avoided Josie's eyes. "Let's take a walk. I want to speak with you."

Before they make their way halfway around the block, he stopped. He stood still. He couldn't look her in the eye. "Marry me, Josie."

She'd prayed for this moment, though the excitement made her heart race. She didn't hesitate. "Yes, Benny. I love you too."

"Oh, that's great, Josie."

"But how are we going to get married? Neither of us has a job. I don't finish high school for two more years."

Benny stayed calm. "I thought it all out. My aunt will put us up in an apartment till I get a job. I start at twenty-five dollars a week, and when I become a journeyman it goes up to sixty. The rent is only thirty dollars a month. Don't worry, Josie. Aunt Molly can drive us to City Hall. We'll have a free, short civil ceremony and it's official. Then you can tell your father all about it. Josie, I'll take good care of you. You won't be disappointed."

After the Friday afternoon ceremony, Josie and Benny spent their honeymoon on the floor of his aunt's house. The next morning, Aunt Molly and Uncle Jim drove the newlyweds' back to Cora Street. Josie trembled but grasped Benny's hand and entered to face her father.

Frank sat in the easy chair. He stared and lit a cigarette. He wasn't used to making his own dinner. A stony mask hid his emotions. He spoke softly. "Where have you been, Josie?"

Trembling, Josie found her voice. "I've got news, father. Benny and I are married."

"Married?"

"Papa, are you happy?"

Frank stood. He kept his mouth shut for a moment. "I'll help you get your things, Josie. Good luck."

Josie cried and wrung her hands.

Frank stacked her belongings on the front porch. Benny carried them to the waiting car.

"Take good care of her, Benny," Frank said by way of goodbye.

The summer ended and it was Charlie's turn to start high school. Frank picked Commerce High because of its proximity to the house. Charlie initially felt the vocation to be a banker, because, like the famous bank robber Willie Sutton, "that's where the money is." Because of the depression, banking had few openings and less money. Cooler heads prevailed. He discovered an interest in basketball, joining the one hundred ten- pound boy's team. The team blossomed with the new, aggressive point guard. They vied for the City Chanpionship. Charlie scored the winning points in the semi-final. The team, endowed with spirit, guts and a good coach, didn't have the most talented players. But they had hard work, team spirit and a little luck. Commerce won the championship that year.

After a brief stint at Commerce, Charlie transferred to Mission High. With his earnings from paper delivery, scrap metal and various and sundry odd jobs, he decided on more elegant transportation. One fall day, he strode into a car dealership. "I like how that new Ford looks. Sir, what's the purchase price of this vehicle?"

The salesman, a kindly man, let him down gently. He couldn't afford a new car.

Ever practical, Charlie accepted the advice cheerfully and looked for an older model. After a thorough inspection and the promise of a new left-rear tire to replace the one on the car, he proceeded to buy an old Model T on terms from the dealer.

The next day, behind the wheel of a brand shiny new used Ford, Charlie drove to school. The crowd of friends and admirers distracted him. He lost his concentration. The right front wheel jumped the curb onto the grass. A teacher witnessed the event. That incident resulted in Charlie looking for a new high school. He didn't mind. His grades were poor, and this would allow a new start. Besides, he had a change of heart. He wanted to become a dentist, and wanted a school that could prepare him.

Frank looked around for a school with a good basketball team. He picked Balboa High. It seemed a good fit. Charlie worked hard and found new motivation to succeed. His grades improved. During the basketball season, he practiced and made the team. During the rest of the year, he held down a job from three to ten PM at the Texaco gas station at Fillmore and Lombard. It paid better than his paper route. He sold his old bicycle at a profit. The station owners allowed him to use the tools for car repairs, and the extra income helped out at home.

Charlie didn't need much sleep. He felt energetic all the time, burning with a drive to succeed. He never accepted mediocrity like some of his friends and fellow students. Charlie began his mission to succeed in life.

Balboa High took pride in their sheet metal shop, and with Charlie's interest in scrap metal, it became a natural attraction. Charlie enrolled in his first high school sheet metal class. Mr. Schultz had instructed Charlie in junior high and noted his potential. He continued the encouragement in high school. Mr. Schultz knew how much to challenge his student's curiosity, and when to back off. He became the young boy's mentor. Although Charlie looked upon it as simply another way to make car repairs, sheet metal work turned into a love of creating an idea and building something from nothing. He loved to think creatively and use his hands.

With praise from Mr. Schultz and the basketball coach, Charlie blossomed his senior year.

After his recognition as a sports star, the dates came easily, whenever he had some free time. Shop took up more of his life, and Mr. Schultz continued his encouragement. After home discussions, Frank asked Mr. Schultz about an apprenticeship in sheet metal after graduation. Charlie felt the vocation, and pursued it vigorously. He liked making things. As luck had it, Mr. Schultz had union connections and facilitated Charlie's entry into sheet metal apprenticeship.

The depression continued the high school graduation year of 1938. Frank made the boys pay rent for their rooms. He needed money for the boy's increasing appetites. The job at PG+E paid less. Charlie didn't mind.

David, used to fancy suits and fast women, complained. Frank didn't budge in his rent demands. The family grew used to what they had- peace, food enough, and some spare change for gasoline and the occasional fling at entertainment.

Governmental programs tried to jump- start the economy with an infusion of money and jobs. Social programs kept the least fortunate from starvation, but the economy languished. The Supreme Court decided New Deal programs like the Works Progress Administration (WPA) were unconstitutional. Something else, much bigger in impact, was necessary to lift the country back to its leadership role in the world.

Charlie graduated with above average grades from Balboa High School, and prepared to enter the real working world with encouragement from Frank and his mentor Mr. Schultz. Never knowing any different, Charlie played with the cards dealt him. Unlike others, he planned on winning big.

A

CHAPTER THIRTEEN

WORLD WAR II

San Francisco, 1939. Sons of immigrants like Charlie Andrews sacrificed for our freedom in the worst global conflict in history.

PACIFIC COAST NAVAL AIR BASE CONTRACTORS

Nazi storm troopers of the "Blitzkrieg" invaded Austria on March twelth 1938. Bloodlessly conquering the country, the Second World War began due to Hitler's psychotic scheme for world domination. Joined by Tojo in Japan and Mussolini in Italy, the triumvirate formed the Axis Powers and threatened to overwhelm the world with their industry, power and organization. Italian Americans rallied to the flag of the U.S.A., turning their backs on Mussolini and their ancestral homeland.

Military and political leaders in the United States planned for participation in the war. Older ships about to be scrapped became lifesavers. They rescued Great Britain from blockade and defeat under the Lend-Lease Act. In 1940, the Selective Service Act picked youth for military service. Army training increased. Jimmy Doolittle debated and experimented with the use of airplanes in combat.

Yet many in the United States, including the aviator hero Charles Lindbergh, vocally touted the virtues of non-alliance. He received widespread support.

"It's Europe's war," Lindbergh said. "Let them fight it."

That attitude withered.

December seventh 1941, "A day that will live in infamy," in the words of President Roosevelt. Japanese airplanes bombed Pearl Harbor in a sneak attack. Now it wasn't just a European war. It was our war. Now, it was personal.

Charlie Andrews, twenty-two years old, couldn't believe the treachery of the Japanese. Angry, because the cowardly Japanese bombed Pearl Harbor in a sneak attack and drew America into the War. He felt shame as an Italian because the motherland of Italy, under the rule of the Fascist Mussolini, fought on the side of the Axis. As an Italian American, his loyalty lay with the USA. Why did the land of his ancestors fight America?

After completing his apprenticeship, Mr. Schultz drew Charlie's attention to the full-page ad in the San Francisco Chronicle. The Pacific Coast Naval Air Base Contractors needed men. *Skilled laborers needed to rebuild and fortify America's defenses.*

He jumped at the opportunity. Since finishing his apprenticeship suited Charlie to this work to help his country, he volunteered to go to Hawaii, see the world, and get decent pay, far beyond wages on the mainland.

The clerk at Pacific Coast Naval Air Base Contractors leaned over the counter. "Great, Mr. Andrews. We can use you. We sail in three weeks, mid-January. Everything is in order. All we need to close the deal is your birth certificate. Get us a copy and you ship out as a journeyman sheet metal worker on the *Permanente*. Congratulations!"

Charlie thought this career looked promising. "Thank you, sir. I'll get right on that. I'll drive to the Public Health Department today and pick up the certificate."

He searched for hours. Finding nothing, he asked the clerk for help. Neither found a birth certificate for Charles Andrews.

Charlie drove home. Frank sat in the kitchen, drinking his homemade wine. "I don't have a birth certificate on file at the records department. I need it for this big job. Dad, do you know anything about this?"

It was a man's house now, with Josie married. Laundry dried in the back yard. Dust collected on the living room floor. Charlie thought he drank too much wine, and a cigarette stayed in his fingers. He ate a bowl of spaghetti. Josie only did the cooking and cleaning on holidays. Frank looked at his son and took his hand. "Sit down. I want you to know I did it for you. You don't realize what kidding we took with Italian names and accents. Everyone made fun. To protect you from that discrimination, I changed the family name from D'Alessandro to Andrews. But your real name, the one on your records, is Marcello D'Alessandro. You don't know it, but that is my name, also."

Charlie smiled, tickled at this hidden sign of love and affection from his father. "That makes me feel good, dad. Now how do I get a birth certificate?"

"When we moved here, before your mother died, we started to use Andrews. I wanted to get the job at PG+E and not suffer discrimination. But I never changed it legally. You have been Charles Frank Andrews all your life, except on the papers. I hope you're not upset. I did it for you."

Charlie needed the birth certificate before shipping out. "Dad, I'm not upset. I have to go back and get the document. They accepted my application. I don't want to lose this job. I leave for Hawaii in three weeks."

Frank hugged his son. "It's there, under the name D'Alessandro. I'm so proud of you. I promise to go to the court and change it legally. I did it for you."

Three weeks later, at sea on the *Permanente*, the weather held. Not many got seasick. Charlie walked out on deck, soaking up the sun. As they did every morning, a group of men discussed the scuttlebutt. "The *SS Emidio* went down eighteen miles off Crescent City, California. Damn Japanese sub sunk her in December."

No one had seen that bit of news printed in the paper. They talked about their chances of reaching Hawaii alive. Charlie had heard about the *SS Cynthia Olson*, the first US ship torpedoed by a Japanese sub on December seventh. The conversation aboard the *Permanente* took on added importance.

Charlie spent more free time on deck, scanning the seas for signs of enemy shipping. Feelings ran high, for personal safety and patriotism.

The scuttlebutt level rose several days out of port. Their foreman, a supervisor for the Pacific Coast Naval Air Base Contractors, called a meeting on deck. All the one hundred workers gathered in sunny, cool weather to hear the news. "Men, I have important information. Your contract specified Johnson Island, far out on the Hawaiian chain. I've been informed the Japanese commenced bombing Johnson yesterday. We've been diverted to Pearl Harbor. The Navy assures the captain we are in no immediate danger. For safety, the captain has increased speed to sixteen knots. We arrive in a day and a half. Expect to see a lot of friendly escorts in the air and on the sea. Any questions?"

Charlie raised his hand. "Does this mean we get combat pay?"

After laughing, the supervisor replied, "Not until you start carrying a rifle."

"You mean rivets and hammers don't qualify?"

That humor faded the day they sailed into Pearl. Charlie cried as the hulk of the battleship *U.S.S. Arizona*, tower visible above the water, signified the reality of this conflict. Far from the island paradise he envisioned, the war transformed the island chain into a fortress and our closest harbor to Japan. He and his shipmates went from workers to valuable war assets. For the next three weeks they tore down wreckage of the Japanese invasion, allowing rebuilding by the Armed Forces. Charlie and his friends took an oath of secrecy to prevent intelligence falling into Japanese hands. The men were warned not to consort with Japanese men or women on the island. Regardless of citizenship, paranoia about spies drove the military government to extreme lengths for security.

After transfer to Barber's Point Naval Air Station on Oahu, the crew built barracks for six months. Charlie appreciated the beauty of the island on his infrequent days off. That assignment completed, they moved to the quieter lee side of the island. Kaneohe Bay Marine Corps Air Station used Charlie and his fellow civilian construction workers for twelve-hour days, seven days a week. They did get a break on housing, and Charlie and the boys frequented the bars, luaus and gambling joints late at night. Poker became his game of choice, and Charlie's poker face and luck held for the eighteen-month stint on Oahu. He and the crew finished infrastructure necessary to extent the war effort beyond Hawaii. With his help, the Navy prepared to take the war to the Japanese.

Steaming to the mainland in June 1943, the construction men discussed the war news they had missed in the isolation of Hawaii. After Jimmy Doolittle's carrier launched bombing raid on Japan, America got up from the mat and fought back. A short time after the Navy won the Battle of Midway in June 1942, they invaded Guadalcanal and took the first of many islands conquered by the Japanese. Charlie and his co-workers felt buoyed by their country's success. Though the Battle of the Atlantic still raged, with German U-boats sinking twenty to thirty Merchant Marine ships daily, Government censorship whitewashed the news. "Two medium Allied transports sunk today" became the standard report from the Navy.

The crew lounged in the mess hall, days away from landfall. They enjoyed their time off after eighteen months of hard labor. Charlie's neighbor sat down for lunch.

"I'll be working in the shipyard," his mess neighbor said. "They build ships in forty-five days. I want to be part of that effort."

Charlie took a folded newspaper ad from is pocket. He showed it to his friends. *"Join the U.S. Maritime Service. Help your country deliver the goods. We need you!"*

The men recognized it, the ads were everywhere. His friend said, "That's an idea. See the world, and no officers on your back. I might like that."

Charlie shook his head. "You get seasick when we go flank speed. The merchant marine is for guys like me who can work in storms and high seas. I think I'll visit this Government Recruiting Office they mention in San Francisco. It might work out."

As the ship docked in Oakland, Charlie finished his dessert and finalized his plans to join the U.S. Maritime Service.

MERCHANT MARINE

Far- sighted engineers drew up plans for a strong Merchant Marine. Knowing the industrial might of America would push the balance towards victory, the armed forces needed reliable transportation to England and Europe. Henry J. Kaiser, construction baron of California, settled on a single, simple, reproducible design and convinced the government it could work. He launched the Liberty Ship line.

Workers built thousands of these identical ships at record pace to carry troops, ammunition, airplanes and raw materials for the Allies. However, following orders of Fleet Admiral Ernest J. King, the Merchant Marine carried little protection. They had inadequate guns, less than adequate escorts. The Merchant Marine lost one in every thirty-two men during the war, mostly in the Atlantic to German U-boats. The U—boats boasted a top speed of sixteen knots, faster than most Merchant Marine ships. Merchant Mariners had the highest casualty rate of any service, exceeding that of the U.S. Marines.

Malicious stories circulated on the home front by the Navy, concerned Merchant Mariners dodging the draft. Mariners became subject to the draft if they took more than thirty days shore leave. A cover-up in the press concerned Merchant Mariner Harold Harper, torpedoed yet again. He received a letter from the FBI and Selective Service after swimming away from his sinking ship for the sixth time. Another deliberate lie tormented the thoughts and feelings of his compatriot Nick Hoogendam, drifting for eighty-three days on a ife-raft drinking rainwater and eating fish. These men did not shirk their responsibilities or resist the nation's efforts to win the war. The Merchant Marine showed remarkable courage and fortitude during this disastrous time for shipping, the *Battle of the Atlantic*.

Charlie enjoyed a brief stay with Frank in Visitacion Valley. Frank's life looked the same. Smoking, work, visiting friends, drinking his wine.

His father praised Charlie's work. The war was on Frank's mind. He was lonely. He wanted his son back. "Son, what will you do now?"

"I'm working on my next job. I've got to do what's right."

"The war is heating up. They ration electricity. There's no rubber for car tires, no gasoline to drive. Even if I had money, I couldn't afford fresh fruit and vegetables. We eat meat only once a week."

"I know, dad. I'll keep sending money each month."

"Thank, son. Don't put yourself in danger. Be careful. We need you here."

Charlie left his father to his life of drinking and smoking. He visited Josie and Benny.

"I'm shipping out tomorrow. Tell dad after I go."

Josie said, "He won't be happy. He wants you here."

Charlie smiled. "I have to go. I lined up a job at the Government Recruiting Office. She's the *Horace Greeley* Liberty Ship."

Benny nodded. "Lots of sheet metal workers are building them over in Oakland. What's she like?"

"The California Shipbuilding Corporation is where your friends work. This ship started July thirty-first to completion on September ninth 1942."

"No wonder those guys get top dollar," Benny said.

"Top speed of twelve knots and a payload capacity of ten thousand tons."

"I love you, Charlie. Good luck."

He kissed Josie, shook Benny's hand, and went home to sleep in a stationary bed.

The next morning, papers in hand, Charlie found the dock in Oakland. This ship was larger than his transport from Hawaii. Workers swarmed around the area, welding and moving cargo. He climbed the plank to the main deck. Crowded with supply crates, metal to finish the air scoops, and people, little room remained for newcomers. "Charlie Andrews reporting for duty."

The seaman looked at his papers. He cast an eye at the young Italian. "Construction and sheet metal, I see. No experience at sea?"

"No, but I'm a quick learner, sir," Charlie said.

"I'm called 'mister.' This isn't the Navy, son," the seaman replied. "I'm here to show you how to do your job. You signed on as a wiper. Any idea what that is?"

Charlie shook his head. He'd never been below decks on a ship.

"Follow me, then."

They proceeded down four decks, deep below the water line. "These are the pressurized doors. Never, I repeat never, allow both doors to open at the same time. The pressure in the engine room is higher to force oxygen into the twin diesels, and keep air from coming down the stacks. I don't want that to happen." The chief entered the air lock, motioning Charlie to follow.

Charlie didn't understand the ranks and levels. Charlie broke out in a sweat. The outer door closed and his ears popped. Then, like a hammer, the inner door opened. Heat, noise and humidity tore his eyes and lungs with raw force. Twin diesel engines cranked slowly, powering up the energy for the ship. Shiny metal glistened in the light. The ship remained stationary, tied to the dock.

The chief screamed over the noise. "You'll get used to it. Right now, it's only a hundred degrees. It can get up to one hundred forty when we pick up speed. Wait till we get to the tropics. Follow me." They walked down two levels to the engines.

Charlie thought his head would explode. Noise caused his ears to ring. Vibration hurt his teeth. His shirt soaked sweat pouring from every pore. As hot, humid, dirty air entered his lungs, his chest tightened. Breathing became difficult.

The chief screamed over the din. "This is what you do for the next four hours, till you're relieved. See that rotating pipe, near your head? Take this can and oil it, then wipe any extra so it doesn't hit the deck and make a mess. Understand?"

Charlie nodded.

"It goes from here," pointing to the engine block, "aft to that tunnel. Eventually it turns the screws, but you don't have to go that far, ha, ha. Any questions?"

Charlie shook his head.

"You're relieved at eight bells. You sleep four hours, and when eight bells rings again, you return to duty. Understand?"

He nodded. "Water?"

"Sure, all the water you need is about two feet outside that hull. But if you need a drink, climb up to that container near the pressure doors. Now, get to work."

Charlie waved to his fellow wiper, busy on the opposite engine. Mimicking his action, he reached up with the oilcan and squirted, which resulted in oil dripping on his hair, face, and neck. He wiped it up before any hit the deck. Looking around, he took a deep breath and thought for a minute. Then he dripped the oil on the upper surface and wiped it along and around.

After several minutes, he changed hands, alternating oilcan and oily rag. He sweat till he couldn't see, and had to wipe his eyes every few minutes.

Then he stopped breathing. Letting both arms down to his side allowed boiling air to enter his parched lungs. Breathing wasn't much relief.

After the eternity of four hours, the chief checked on him. Charlie stumbled up the first flight, barely made it to the second. As the first pressurized door closed behind him, every fiber of his being wanted to open the outside. The voice of the chief in his head reminded him never, never open the door till the pressure equalized.

Charlie stumbled two more decks up to his quarters. Before falling into the bed, he asked the chief a question. "I'd like permission to string up a hammock outside. I can relax better in the open air. The cabin is stuffy."

"Just don't get washed overboard," the chief replied.

The *Horace Greeley* set to sea shortly after Charlie's first shift. The chief mentioned their cargo consisted of ten thousand pounds of munitions for the war effort in Australia.

Weeks later, after Charlie first crossed the Equator, he became a member of the Neptune Society. All the initiates endured the naval ritual of shaving the head of all hair. Charlie was then considered a full-fledged member of the crew. The *Horace Greeley* docked in Hobart, Tasmania.

The harbor stayed on full war alert.

The threat of Japanese submarines forced the harbormaster to deviate from customary procedures. The *Horace Greeley's* ten thousand pounds of munitions convinced the harbormaster to keep them isolated at anchor in the middle of the harbor till fully unloaded. Weeks at sea and they still remained prisoners on board. Charlie, twenty pounds lighter, with thinning hair and little money, rubbed his sore stomach. Digestive difficulties.

After a week spent unloading the hold of ammunition, loaded onto ferries for the trip to shore, the captain gave the word. The ship pulled into dock. Trucks filled with ammunition from the *Horace Greeley* sped to Perth to aid General MacArthur, training for an assault on the Japanese.

The next day, the crew lined up outside the purser's office. The purser wouldn't be rushed.

"Andrews."

He sweat with the rest of them, waiting for his pay and mail.

"Here."

"Your pay. You've earned eight hour of shore leave. Be back for your shift."

"Yes indeed. I'm ready."

The purser, a friend, gave Charlie a smirk. "Don't get into any trouble. The captain will have your head if you screw up."

The nearest bar filled with friendly Aussies happened to have a poker game. Charlie sat in front of a stack of US and Australian money. Benny Goodman's music played in the background. Everyone craved beer. Some danced with the locals.

As the others drank, Charlie studied their faces and mannerisms. This poker was a job he thoroughly enjoyed. The game went on and his winnings doubled. He boarded the *Horace Greeley* at four bells, none the worse for wear. Before entering the confines of the engine room, he put his winnings into an envelope and addressed it to Frank Andrews on Cora Street, then gave it to the chief to mail.

Charlie saw new and wonderful sights. From Hobart to Perth, Australia, on to Calcutta, Madras and Bombay, India and then Capetown, South Africa, working in the sweat—box of the engine room didn't pass quickly. The crew worked hard. Anxiety at sea alternated with relief in port. War news came slowly as was the custom of the US counter-intelligence agency. German submarines remained a constant threat to the Merchant Marine anywhere in the Atlantic, north and south. Away from home for eighteen months, Charlie wondered if he'd ever return to America. He and his crewmates grew home-sick and anxious about the progress of the war.

The Navy learned the importance of convoys and destroyers to guard merchant ships the hard way. With each technical and tactical advance, German U-boat commanders, capable of sixteen knots on the surface, changed tactics. Point and counterthrust. No commander anticipated a safe day in the Atlantic, since the Liberty Ship's top speed remained twelve knots. Worse, the war effort seemed stalled. The Allied counterattack in North Africa went poorly. Rommel cleverly avoided entrapment in the desert. Germany looked invincible.

The captain announced the *Horace Greeley* would travel across open ocean from Capetown to Trinidad and Guyana. The convoy consisted of eighty ships. Charlie and his mates had mixed feelings. Though the news of their return to the Western Hemisphere was welcome, he and the crew realized the perils of a convoy across the Atlantic. U-boat country.

As the *Horace Greeley* started the Atlantic run, Charlie settled into a routine. Work, food, sleep, and scan the seas. The men did anything they could to help. Charlie saw nothing during daylight but friendlys.

Barely one day out of Cape Town, seventy-nine ships remained. He hadn't heard a warning the ship went down. The next morning at dawn he counted them out. Only seventy merchantsremained.

U-boats increased their activity as they moved farther from land. After dusk, the German subs surfaced, recharged their batteries and coordinated their attack. Fully charged, they submerged and attacked, using the first crippled ship as a shield to attack others with impunity. Charlie cursed as the *Horace Greeley* passed Americans in distress. Convoy rules forbade other merchant ships from stopping to help a sinking ship. It made them too easy a target for the deadly U-boats. No one slept during the slaughter. Who's number would come up tonight?

Charlie's morning scan of the horizon counted the toll.

Midway in the voyage, losses mounted. The Liberty Ships meager defenses, small deck-mounted guns, couldn't match a sub. Only the destroyers carried depth charges and sonar. Charlie heard a nearby ship get hit by a German torpedo. Trapped in the bowels of the ship made his stomach tie up in knots. The sounds of the ship breaking up, transmitted through the thick sea—water, caused nausea.

The carnage continued.

After three weeks at sea and the loss of hundreds of men, forty ships limped into Panama. The other forty paid the price of war, finding their resting place on the ocean floor. The lucky survivors unloaded in the Panama Canal Zone. Charlie and the rest of the crew celebrated their lives and mourned the loss of so many good men. Shore leave lost its glamour.

When the ship docked in New Orleans, its first American port since San Pedro California, Charlie had enough. In the good graces of the chief, with his papers as a wiper, fireman and water tender in order, he left the ship and took a vacation in New Orleans. He swore never to eat beans and hardtack again. Then, with poker winnings from several long games, he boarded a train to San Francisco, with a short stop in Colorado to visit James Cull, a friend from San Francisco.

Charlie knocked on the door on Teddy Street in the early evening before sundown. His father answered.

"Son, you are back from the sea." Frank's jaw dropped. He pounded his thin, lean son on the back.

"I'm glad to be back, dad."

Frank picked up the telephone. "Josie, come quickly, Charlie is home."

Neighbors up and down from Frank's new house came by to give their regards. Frank had talked incessantly about his son. Everyone wanted to see him in the flesh. Frank brought out his best wine. Family and friends crowded on the back porch of the tiny house with a great view of the bay. Frank cried.

His son returned alive.

Charlie regaled them with stories from ports on the other side of the world.

A neighbor asked, "How are we doing in the war?"

"Winning. I can tell you some things that might make you lose your hair," he replied, rubbing his balding head, "but I can't tell you everything. Security, you know."

The neighbor didn't laugh. He knew the phrase *Loose lips sink ships* only too well.

Josie rejoiced at the reunion. She continued to feel a mother's love for her closest brother. His money from overseas kept the family afloat financially. "We missed you, Charlie. The whole neighborhood is proud of you. Tell us what happened at sea."

Charlie relaxed as he sat outside among friends. Though winter, the San Francisco weather looked clear, with no precipitation. He didn't have to worry about eight bells, or U-boats. But the war continued and those at home were concerned. Everyone sacrificed on the home front.

Rather than tell whitewashed stories of his voyage, he stole furtive glances at Frank. Charlie worried at his father's appearance. Thinner, coughing, he drank too much wine. Charlie winced as his father blew cigarette smoke his way during a conversation. He seemed irritable.

Frank and the neighbors thirsted for validation their sacrifices helped the USA win, that it would end up all right. They heard little from the newspaper. Newsreels came months late. Charlie told them what they wanted to hear. The story of his convoy stayed under his hat. But he had plenty of other stories to tell.

Frank's irritability improved for a short while. After the first story, Frank went to bed. He had to work the next day. His routine never varied.

The next day's mail changed Charlie's plans. Josie brought him the letter marked *US Selective Service for Charles Frank Andrews*. The government needed men for the Army infantry. She cried. "Charlie, what does it mean? Dad and I couldn't have made it without the money you sent us. Times have been hard here, but everyone, most of all the Italians, work hard to support our country. What will you do?"

They sat in the kitchen on Teddy Street, eating an early lunch. Fingering the unopened letter, Charlie smiled. "I think I'll join the Navy. I don't see myself in a foxhole. With my construction experience and good report from the Merchant Marine, I'll have no trouble."

Josie frowned. "Is that safer than the Army?"

154

"I want to tell you, Josie, I'm going to be above the water line at all times on this cruise. No more engine room for me."

"Anything but the Army," Josie said. "They're all talking about the big invasion of Europe since General Patton beat the Germans in North Africa and Sicily. The neighbors have gotten word from their relatives in Italy. They say it will be very big. Don't go in the Army, Charlie."

He read the letter in private. "You are ordered to report to Selective Service. If found fit for duty you will be assigned to Fort Dix, New Jersey. Obey this order under penalty of arrest."

He made up his mind. It was an easy decision.

UNITED STATES NAVY

The next day, accompanied by his father and sister, Charlie bypassed the Selective Service office and went directly to the Navy recruiter. With his experience and credentials, they took him with open arms. He would go back to sea, this time in uniform. At least he had an idea of what to expect, and he was happy to avoid the Army.

First came basic training.

Navy training in the middle of winter at Coeur d'Alene Idaho shocked Charlie's system. Used to stifling tropical heat, he held a wooden gun and guarded a crossroads filled with ten feet of freshly fallen snow in the middle of Idaho. He begged for other, warmer duty. Something inside, near a heater, bending sheet metal and constructing. He wasn't used to the cold.

He was re-assigned to the sheet metal shop.

Charlie volunteered for gunnery school after graduation. His assignment to the Newport, Rhode Island gunnery school as a seaman Second class went smoothly. He figured if he was going to be on deck with those Kamikazes buzzing around, he might as well shoot back. They lived in Quonset huts and ate real food. Over the weeks, he practiced on the twenty mm guns, learning to identify the rhythmic *ach-ach-ach*. Soon, he was able to identify the ammunition from the color code, distinguishing tracer rounds from those exploding at various altitudes.

For the next assignment came the bigger, powerful forty mm's. Unlike the alto twenty's, they made a baritone's *tom-tom-tom* much louder. The Navy put him through hours of target practice, learning to estimate altitude, leading the dummy planes so the shells could collide and knock down the enemy. After completing his rating on the twenty and forty mm deck guns, he received his assignment. He didn't plan on damage to his hearing from the noise of those big guns.

Charlie's gunnery rating took on added significance. The focus of the war changed for the Navy. On June sixth 1944 the invasion of Europe commenced, with General Eisenhower in supreme command. The men in gunnery school realized the success of Operation Overlord in Europe meant they would go to the Pacific. MacArthur of the Army and Halsey and Spruance of the Navy needed reinforcements for their island hopping strategy to invade Japan. Everyone knew about the long struggle for Guadalcanal. It would be a bloody battle to the death for the Japanese. The enemy fought for each inch of jungle in the South Pacific. That's where the Navy needed men and ships.

Charlie received his orders and arrived by train in Norfolk. The *U.S.S. Casa Grande* (LSD-13) bobbed at anchor in the Norfolk Navy Yard. Having completed her shakedown cruise in Chesapeake Bay, she armed and trained her new crew. After the fitness rating, she readied for immediate departure.

Charlie couldn't believe his eyes. Built specifically for the Normandy invasion, which the first dozen of its class attended, the *Casa Grande* possessed unique features. Her cargo hold had capacity for several dozen landing craft. In the event of an amphibious invasion, she flooded the lower well deck and sunk deeper into the water. Gigantic aft floodgates opened, and the landing craft floated out one at a time under their own power to the beach or harbor. Charlie had never seen such a ship.

Charlie approached the officer in charge of boarding. His uniform spotless, they saw immediately he was a FNG (freaking new guy). "Charles Andrews, seaman 2nd class, reporting for duty, sir."

The officer sat at a small deck on the dock, checking papers. "At ease, seaman. Welcome to the *Casa Grande*."

"Thank you, sir."

Scanning his record, the Lieutenant saw Charlie's prowess with sheet metal and boat repairs. "We can use a good man with your skills, Andrews. You'll have part time duty in the metal shop, when not manning the guns. One other thing. You ever made a deck chair?"

Charlie saw the smile on the officer's face. "No problem, sir. What would you like it to look like?"

The officer looked around. He wasn't regular Navy, but from the reserve officer squadron. "Nothing fancy, we're at war. But something small and comfortable, so I can relax on deck during good weather."

As they sailed from Norfolk on July thirteenth 1944, Charlie watched as the officers sat in identical chairs, sunning while off duty. The officers allowed him to string up his hammock on the deck during good weather, after he told them how claustrophobic the cabin seemed. They shared the latest news. The ship had orders for the Pacific.

Good weather accompanied them and their escort vessels through the Panama Canal to Charlie's old stomping grounds, Pearl Harbor. Most of the crew had never seen the famous tropical island. During their surreptitious weekly poker game, Charlie told stories. "Yes, they really do the hula. It's hard to believe, in that hot sun, how they shimmy and shake. Those Hawaiian girls aren't skinny, they're built for work. The sweat just pours off, the music goes faster and faster, then it's over. You boys will have to see it to believe it. I hope we get some shore leave."

His luck at poker continued.

Filled with twenty landing craft, combat loaded with medium tanks and personnel, the captain ordered exercises in fleet maneuvers, anti-aircraft firing, and signal drills.

The officers made no bones about their fear of Kamikaze attack. Charlie's aim on the forty—mm gun improved steadily. He learned to follow the tracer rounds to lead the targeted aircraft. The farther they ventured into enemy territory, the more he tuned into the deep tom-tom-tom of those forty's. His life and the lives of all aboard might depend on his aim. Charlie complained to his buddies about the long hours and boring repetition.

The officers complimented Charlie on his aim.

His friend "Cousin" Homer set up the occasional poker game. The enlisted men played in secret over the engine room escape hatch. Charlie was always invited. The officers never found out where Charlie made all his earnings.

The ships in battle formation cruised through the South Pacific never spotting a Japanese submarine. They arrived at Eniwetok, the Marshall Islands, on September twenty-four. Blue water of the atoll harbor constituted a mid—way refueling port for the trans-Pacific journey. The men set their feet down on soft white sand. While there the Yap invasion was cancelled.

Charlie approached his officer in charge. "I hate to waste all that training. What do we do now, lieutenant?"

"Don't worry, Andrews. We'll put it to good use."

Charlie offered the officer another Mai Tai. "Do you know where we're headed?"

"Yes."

"Sir, how about some tropical nuts?"

"Listen, you men. Keep this to yourself. We are heading for Leyte Gulf, the Philippine Islands. That's the biggest Jap harbor on Leyte Island, a large island in the Philippine chain. Macarthur plans to invade. He's trying to keep the promise he made to the Philippino people, 'I shall return.' We're going to soften up the Japs for him."

"I wouldn't mind spending more time here, on the beach."

"You keep practicing with the forty mm," the officer warned. "Kamikaze activity is heavy. They do more damage every day, and not only to the battleships and carriers. Our ship will be in constant danger of attack during this operation."

Maneuvers intensified in the tropical heat. Tempers flared during long hours of drills. The *Casa Grande* arrived at the staging area for the attack. With those hours of gunnery practice, Charlie's confidence rose as the first day of the invasion dawned. His first experience of an amphibious invasion introduced him to the noise, confusion and uncertainty of war. "We arrived at Blue Beach, Letye, Philippine Islands at 01030 October twenty 1944. We debarked troops and landing craft on schedule with no casualties. Action seemed light till 1500 when Japanese planes attacked. I commanded one of our fortymm guns, firing furiously. The rhythmic action and 'tom-tom-tom' of the guns reassured me. We didn't down any planes. One of the Japs torpedoed the *U.S.S. Honolulu* only two thousand yards off our starboard side. The concussion, and resulting fire on the *Honolulu* scared us all. That being my first action under fire, I felt happy to survive, and satisfied with my performance on the guns.

"The enemy continued their attack during our departure. Two planes dove and singled us out. We drove them off with our fortymm's, all except my gun. One of my gun crew suffered stress under fire. He was unable to comply with the order to fire. The lieutenant asked me about it, and I gave him a complete report. That was the last I heard about it."

As enemy air attacks abated, the *Casa Grande* withdrew. Some on the crew dared relax. The crew dealt with stress individually. Damage report showed none. Their duties at Leyte completed, they set out on a cargo run.

The crew hadn't counted on Nature herself as an enemy. "During a ferry run from Tacloban, Leyte, south to Hollandia, New Guinea in late October, we entered a tropical storm low pressure disturbance. It grew into a typhoon. We found our convoy caught in its full force. Wind, monster waves over thirty feet high and rain decreased visibility to nothing. The ship, caught in the heavy swell, rolled precipitously. A buddy explained how, with a big enough roll, water entered the stacks and extinguished the engines. Without power the ship would capsize. That was an automatic death knoll. We rolled as much as forty-seven degrees at times, about as near the fatal point as possible without taking water down the stacks. The waves were brutal. No one could sleep with the pounding. The night of terror continued till dawn. The next morning the weather cleared.

"We received the news we lost two destroyers, capsized in the ferocity of the storm. None of the men aboard survived."

-

At remote South Pacific ports of call, the crew enjoyed shore leave. Free time, fresh food and booze allowed the stressed men to kick back. The contrast was difficult, from invasion to storm to quiet port of call. Charlie developed a working friendship with the commander of the lower decks, named Schwab, who answered only to the Captain. He often gave Charlie a break. Charlie reciprocated any time he asked.

On November ninth, the Casa Grande anchored at Hollandia, Dutch New Guinea on a blue, mid-summer tropical morning. Commander Schwab asked Charlie to drive his barge. They cruised across port to another supply vessel undergoing repairs. "Charlie, stay close. I've got a good friend on this ship. I'll call you when I'm ready to return. We like to drink, so be ready."

After a nap, Charlie used the binoculars to scan the fleet. He unpacked a lunch and ate. After another nap he got antsy. Boarding the supply vessel, he asked permission to board. "Have you seen Commander Schwab?"

"Down in the hold. They're making a lot of noise."

Charlie found his friend Schwab stinking drunk. He jury rigged a boson's chair and lowered Schwab into the barge. A quick trip across the harbor brought them to the *Casa Grande*.

The Casa Grande had no boson's chair. Charlie didn't want Schwab embarrassed if the Captain came on deck. Charlie waved to the men on deck. "Lower a cargo net."

Minutes later it dropped into the barge. Moving the comatose Schwab into the middle, he secured the corners. "All right, heave."

They hauled Schwab onto the deck. Charlie took him to the officers' quarters and put him to bed.

Schwab returned to duty three days later. Mission accomplished.

-

Charlie knew what he wanted to do when shore leave was granted. He and his friends played poker. They picked a restaurant where they could play in peace, get dinner, and sleep if time allowed. Charlie took whatever winnings he made and dropped them in the mail to Teddy Street.

Many of the crew had difficulty with nerves. They looked for the local girls. There were plenty, all dreaming of marrying an American and leaving their tiny islands at war's end. Some of the drunks wound up married, causing complications when the ship sailed away. There were no enemy attacks during their voyages. The summer heat of November and December baked those left on deck during guard duty. For a short while, it didn't seem like war anymore. It felt more like a vacation.

The routine changed in late 1944. The ship made continuous trips between the Philippines, Hollandia, and Manus of the Admiralty Islands. The brass planned another invasion.

Training commenced in earnest. As tension rose on the decks, so did nerves. The crewmen worked till they couldn't stand.

Charlie got the word of their destination around Christmas from his lieutenant. "It's another Philippine invasion. We're moving north to Luzon."

"Thanks, sir. Where's Luzon."

"It's a larger island and home of the pre-war Philippine government. MacArthur's army was based there before the war."

Charlie spread the word. The men didn't complain about target practice.

"On nine January 1945 we entered Lingayen Gulf, Luzon, Philippine Islands under cover fire. With precision and speed we discharged our troops and equipment, without casualty. During our sortie, enemy planes attacked. We opened fire with our five/thirty-eights and forty mm's. We drove them off before they did any damage. No planed shot down."

Charlie fired all his ammunition during the attack. The *tom-tom-tom* and explosions burned an indelible image into his eyes.

After the invasion, Charlie received a call from his superior officer to report to the officers quarters immediately.

"What do they want me for?"

"I don't know, sailor. Just get there double-time."

The ensign's cabin in the officers' quarters doubled as an office. The ensign and he looked about the same age. "Andrews, sir. Reporting as ordered."

"Andrews. At ease."

Charlie hated these summons to the officers quarters. It might be just another order for a deck chair. On the other hand, it might be a reprimand or assignment below decks. "Yes, sir."

The officer was a busy man. "Your work on the forty mm's has been exemplary. You have a new assignment. You will deploy with our tank transporting landing craft, the LCM, and man their twenty mm. You have your rating on the twenties, don't you?"

"Yes sir, from gunnery school in Newport, Rhode Island."

"Good. Your job is to keep the boat safe so the Marine tanks can land on the beach. Understood?"

"Yes, sir."

"Keep up the good work, Andrews. Dismissed."

"Yes, sir, and thank you, sir." Not knowing what this meant, Charlie beat a hasty retreat.

When off duty, Charlie felt a little unsure. During a poker game he questioned his friends. "Fellas, what do you think is safer? Firing a forty mm from the deck of the ship at a Kamikaze, or using a twenty mm on a landing craft to shoot machine gun nests on the beach?"

They laughed. "Neither, Charlie. Just relax and take a card. You need to follow orders. Don't think about your safety during an amphibious invasion. It will drive you crazy. Either the bullet has your name on it or it doesn't. Only God above decides."

The poker players quieted. They approached another close contact with war. Would their luck hold?

The Casa Grande cruised on a routine supply run.

"Battle stations. Battle Stations."

The ship came under heavy attack, including Kamikazes.

"I guess even officers make mistakes," Charlie muttered as he put on the headset. He and the gun crew awaited firing orders for the forty mm. In the worsening light of dusk, a plane marked with the Rising Sun slip through the anti-aircraft fire. Moments later the U.S.S. Shadwell exploded one thousand yards off the starboard quarter.

"Open fire!"

Charlie screamed at his crew, turning his eyes away from the Shadwell towards the hostiles. "Starboard quarter, focus behind the wreck. There. Let's get him, boys!"

The pounding tom-tom-tom of the forty mm's deafened them for an instant. Hot casings fell to the deck. Encased in pitch- black darkness, every third shell a tracer, the action seemed like a meteor shower.

Until the enemy plane burst into flames.

Charlie led the cheers of his gun crew. "We got him. We scored the kill!"

Ears ringing, mouths dry, Charlie and the crew watched in slow motion as the Japanese Kamikaze crashed into the sea off their port quarter. As the action concluded they streamed below and discussed the action. Adrenaline flowed in the mess as they discussed their first kill as a team. Other crews came by and pounded them on the back. After seeing the <u>Shadwell</u> hit, they realized it might have been them. "Great job, Charlie. Our turn next time," they vowed. "Keep up the great shooting."

*

In February 1945 the Casa Grande found anchor in Tassaforganga, Guadalcanal, Solomon Islands. Well southeast of the action, this port call came as welcome relief. Perhaps another extended shore leave on a tropical atoll. The crew prepared to stand down.

The officer announced the orders. "Our sixteen LCM's will sail to the beach, load the medium tanks, and return to the well deck. Andrews, accompany this detail on the twenty mm gun."

Tassaforganga hadn't seen action for many months. It remained a staging ground for the Marines.

As they hit the beach in the LCM, Charlie received permission from the pilot to go ashore. A cool tropical breeze kept the temperature comfortable. Blue water met white sand. Less than thirty yards away sat coconut trees and shade. Charlie ran into a Marine tank commander, lounging on the beach and looking for a little fun.

"So, you boys will ferry us to the action," the Marine smirked. Crew cut, muscular but thin, he smoked a cigarette while working on his already dark tan.

"Wherever you need to go, we'll get you there," Charlie answered. "Kamikaze's or not."

The Marine offered a cigarette. "Hi, name's Harry Knowles. I heard the little suicide pilots are getting bolder. Have any news about their tactics?"

"My gun crew shot one out of the sky. I saw the whites of his eyeballs as he hit the ocean. That guy was a Chrysanthemum, the trained and equipped branch. They're dying quickly, so tactics are changing."

Knowles took a long drag. "What are they throwing at us now?"

"They're launching the Cherry blossom type. No training, little wood planes, you never can tell what they will do. A wing and a prayer and they hit the ship. Scares the shit out of me, but I guess that's war. I'm Charlie Andrews." He shook Knowles hand.

"Well, Andrews, I never trust a man says he's not scared in war. Pleased to meet you. I command one of these little tanks. I'm getting hot on this damn beach. Got room on your boat?"

After Lt. Colonel Denig, commander of the Sixth Marine Division gave his blessing, Charlie collected a dozen bananas, some coconuts and the tank aboard the LCM.

Charlie remembered the Marine's advice. At they set out to sea on one March 1945, the captain addressed the crew. "Along with the *U.S.S. Cambria and Panamint*, we are designated Attack Group Able. As part of Task Group fifty-three, we will commence training for the coming operation to take Okinawa."

Knowles mapped out his knowledge for the sailors. Further north than the Philippines, Okinawa consisted of a heavily fortified string of coral islands. With three airfields, ten thousand planes and untold numbers of Japanese infantry in bunkers and caves, the Japanese saw the coming battle as their way to stop the US and regain their lost empire. It would be a war of attrition. "Our flyboys want those airfields. With them, our bombers can reach Japan. This is a fight to the death for one side."

The crew hoped that side was Japan.

Knowles grinned and swilled his beer. "Andrews, working you pretty hard, are they?"

"Yes, those guns require lots of practice."

"Did the captain forget your beauty rest? You guys almost woke me up last evening. All that shooting and shouting."

"Listen, Marine, I do my job," Charlie smiled back. "You better get used to the sound of those guns. They are the only thing between you and the deep blue sea. Now, the captain said to be nice to you bums. Why don't you join our poker game tonight? It's a nice, friendly game, and you might learn something other than how to drink."

"Why, that is sporting of you. Mind if I bring a friend?"

An hour later, the Marines arrived at the secret area, away from the officers, drunker than usual. Money bulged from Knowles pockets, and he got right down to business.

"Just us four? Fine with me, as long as your friend has money, Andrews. This is Tom, gunner on my tank. Let's play."

After the introductions, they played in earnest. The Marines seemed too drunk to care, and the Navy won the first several hands. "Straight poker, that's what we play here on the *Casa Grande*," Charlie informed them. "You guys play much?"

"Been too busy fighting," Knowles replied. That stopped the banter for a minute. "But we'll get our timing back soon, right Tom? We made a bundle before the last invasion."

The Marines placed their bets and took their cards. They didn't seem too worried. Perhaps the coming invasion influenced their strategy.

Charlie dealt, kept quiet, and continued winning. The Marines didn't have a chance. After ninety minutes the game halted due to lack of credit.

"Probably just as well," Knowles said. "We hit Ulithi tomorrow and get a day off this God forsaken boat. Then it's on to Okinawa. You know where that is Andrews? Only a hop, skip and bomber flight from downtown Tokyo."

"Yes, I know," Charlie replied. "And it's going to be hot for us both."

The men parted, respectful of each other. They made final preparations a few hours later in Ulithi. The captain ordered constant practice to fend off Kamikaze attack. Charlie stuffed his winnings and a note to Josie in an envelope and sent it home. Then he went out and fired the forty mm till the *tom-tom-tom* made his ears ring.

On twenty-six March 1945, as the air and naval bombardment of Okinawa commenced, the *Casa Grande* left Ulithi, sailing northwest to Okinawa. The plan, to bomb the island, its fortified positions, and four all weather airfields for seven days straight, fooled no one.

The Japanese crawled underground to wait it out. Most of the elite troops pulled back to defend the airfields, leaving less opposition on the beach. Kamikaze pilots, numbering four thousand, prayed to their Emperor and readied themselves for their final, terrible sacrifice. The Japanese knew their situation: this was their last opportunity to save the homeland from invasion and defeat. They possessed six thousand other planes with well-trained pilots to use against the Allies. Two Japanese aircraft carriers joined the fleet defending Okinawa.

If the Japanese lost Okinawa, less than four hundred miles away lay Tokyo, in range of Allied bombers. An Army invasion of Japan would follow imminently. The enemy soldiers prayed to their Emperor and readied themselves to die.

The Americans knew what price they might pay for that privilege.

-

Charlie stayed close to the forty mm the whole cruise from Ulithi, but had no occasion to fire. At four AM on Easter Sunday, third April 1945 the captain gave the order for battle stations. Bombardment with air and the battleship's fourteen-inch Naval guns commenced. An otherworldly clamor descended on the fleet. Destroyers laid down a smokescreen along the beach. At 0830 Charlie left his forty mm and walked to the well deck.

He climbed aboard his LCM as the *Casa Grande* approached Green Beach Two. Their little steel boat was only big enough for one tank and several Marine infantry. The bow hatch, reinforced to ward off enemy fire from the beach, clamped shut. The hatch would open straight forward on the beach, forming a ramp for the tank. Charlie spotted the Marines, already aboard.

Knowles sat on top of the tank, sweating. "So, they got you off the big gun, Andrews. How does it feel?"

"I don't mind telling you, it's strange out there. Complete silence. The smoke so thick you can't see the rising sun. Seas are calm, nice flat beach. How about you, Knowles?"

The Marine looked at him and smiled. "Like I told you, I don't trust a man who's not afraid of combat."

The powerful noise of the pumps interrupted speech. Tons of seawater spilled into the well deck of the *Casa Grande*. The LCM lifted off the metal and floated. Filled with tank and Marines, the first pilot started the engine. Charlie's boat was next in line. They waited, diesel fumes filling the hold, nervous sweat clogging the pores.

At 0845, the massive aft hatches of the *Casa Grande* swung open. Charlie first heard the droning sound of a Kamikaze. As the Allied bombardment abated, explosions filled the air. The enemy fired back. He readied his twenty mm gun, checked the ammo supply and tensed for the trip to the beach. In seconds he spotted their destination, Area Love on Green Beach. The air smelled dirty, filled with smokescreen from the destroyers. The noise of the LCM's drowned out small arms fire and aircraft. Charlie scanned the skies by habit, searching for Kamikaze activity. They ranged about twelve hundred yards from shore. Fanning out, the six LCM's from the Casa Grande opened up the engines, joined by hundreds of craft from other ships. With their human cargo, the landing craft sped towards the unknown terrors on Green Beach. Charlie remembered Knowles advice.

He focused on his twenty mm.

Narrowing the gap to the beach, Charlie heard small arms fire. Enemy fire seemed light from five hundred yards out. No threat to his craft, though he tensed for action closer in. He took a quick look down at the tank crew, poised and ready, engine idling, waiting for the order to disembark. The LCM bore down on the beach. Charlie saw American Marines on his right and Japanese soldiers on the left. The pilot gave the order to ready for landing. Charlie shot the twenty mm *ach-ach-ach-ach-ach*, sweeping the beach before them. Hot spent shells hit the metal of the boat. He kept up a steady fire, clearing the beach directly off the bow.

With a gut-wrenching sound, the LCM rammed a submerged obstacle short of the beach. Their progress stopped abruptly. The pilot lowered the bow hatch to allow the tank egress. After lowering three quarters, it stuck in that position.

The boat sat, immobile and exposed to enemy fire. Trapped on yards of sand, Charlie surveyed the situation. Gunfire to his right between a Japanese machine gun and Marines on the beach attracted his attention. He scanned the berm to his left. A glint of reflected sun revealed a Japanese tank, directed away from them down the beach. It sat on the opposite side of the berm. One of the enemy soldiers pointed at him.

The enemy tank commander smelled a sitting duck.

Knowles head popped out of the tank. "Andrews, what do you see?"

Charlie reported the carnage while firing the twenty mm. "We're stuck short of the beach, about fifteen yards from the berm. Looks like the impact damaged us. The forward hatch is inoperable. I see a Jap tank. They spotted us and are closing fast."

Ach-ach-ach-ach, then silence.

Knowles jumped on top of the tank. He spotted the return fire and yelled into the tank to Tom the gunner.

Charlie found the range. The firefight continued, enemy shells bounding off the metal of the LCM. Several enemy soldiers ran towards them, grenades in hand.

With a powerful "BOOM", the Marine tank's gun exploded in flame. The round hit the enemy tank, silencing it and killing the three- man crew. The Marine tank took off, running through several feet of seawater to the beach. Charlie felt the LCM move off the sand. They drifted. *Ach-ach-ach*, then silence. He ran out of ammunition.

The bow hatch remained locked in full extension, knocked down by the tanks egress. Charlie witnessed a terrifying view of the battle on the island. Water trickled into the LCM from the bow. "Gun it in reverse. See if the shot dislodged us from the sand."

Instead of instant response from the engine, they heard a slow groaning noise. The pilot yelled, "Damn Marines! The tank forced the screws into the sand. They sound badly damaged. We may not make it back."

The LCM moved from the sand, ten yards, now twenty. Charlie watched, helpless. The pilot tried to raise the forward hatch to no avail. No more than a trickle of water flowed in when they stayed in reverse. Aborting the usual configuration, the pilot continued in reverse away from the beach. The clunk, clunk, clunk of the propeller continued, along with the smell of burning oil.

Was it too badly damaged to reach the ship?

Charlie and the pilot turned. The *Casa Grande* lay a long way off. They continued at quarter speed, in reverse, gradually whittling away at the intervening fifteen hundred yards to the ship. Gunfire on the beach, air skirmishes overhead, and battleships lobbing fourteen—inch shells from farther out surrounded them in slow motion. As the LCM approached the *Casa Grande*, the pilot cut the engines. They drifted till grasped by the powerful cranes of the mother ship, and lifted like a baby bird off the ocean onto the deck.

Charlie scanned the sky for signs of a Kamikaze attack. Jumping out of the LCM, he returned to his post on the forty mm deck gun. He felt safer behind the sights of the big gun, the *tom-tom-tom* reassuring him that no Kamikaze would get through his gunfire. Not after what he'd been through.

The *Casa Grande* patrolled the area for the next three days. She directed all small craft of Transport Group Able. Charlie worked double duty, alternately commanding the forty mm and working on small boat repair. His expertise in sheet metal aided the effort to return every possible LCM to transport duty. Charlie waved as an LCM, repaired by his skill in the workshop, loaded a tank and joined the other Marines of the Sixth Division on the beach.

The Japs on shore came out of their fortifications at night. The Marines needed every available man and tank to secure the beachhead. To aid the assault on the beach, the Captain moved the ship less than eight hundred yards offshore. Exposed by their precarious position just off the Okinawa beach, the *Casa Grande* was a big target.

As Charlie reported for gun duty, he saw the Rising Sun. "Incoming! Ready to fire on my command."

The enemy air attack commenced. Well trained, Charlie focused and led the incoming planes with his forty mm fire. *Tom-tom-tom-tom.* Heavy fire drove the Kamikaze pilots away. They realized they had no chance to hit the ship. Charlie's attention was fully taken by the plane off the starboard quarter, spotted by most of the gun crews. Unfortunately, spotters on other Navy ships saw the same plane and opened fire. Caught in a murderous cross- fire, Charlie directed his crew to stand down and take cover. Within seconds, friendly fire wounded three personnel of the *Casa Grande*. The Kamikaze plane hit the ocean and sunk. Charlie watched as the radar pickets *Calhoun* and *Bush* sank by the Kamikaze attack.

Good news came from halfway around the world. On May eighth 1945 Germany surrendered. V-E Day! America focused on the Pacific and brought all her might to bear against the Japanese.

After a job well done, the ship and crew were ordered to Pearl and thence San Francisco. The *Casa Grande* arrived at Moore's Drydock Company, Oakland, for voyage repairs.

During shore leave Charlie and the crew heard about the *Fat Boy* super weapon, the atomic bomb dropped on Hiroshima on August eighth. Days later he read about Nagasaki devastated by the second atomic bomb. Frightened and confused by the power unleashed by these atomic weapons, the men of the *Casa Grande* cheered. There would be no invasion!

The *Casa Grande's* war was over.

V-J (Victory in Japan) Day came on September second 1945. General MacArthur, standing on the deck of the battleship *Missouri* in Tokyo harbor accepted the Emperor's sword. Complete and unconditional surrender.

World War II ended.

A

CHAPTER FOURTEEN

POST WAR BOOM

San Francisco, 1946. With his father's encouragement, Charlie Andrews set out to accomplish his goals.

After honorable discharge from the Navy in 1946, Charlie returned to San Francisco He had his ear to the ground. Mature, seasoned and ambitious, he noted the millions of people who passed through San Francisco during the War. Many came to stay. He read about the post-War economy, powered by babies, pent—up demand for consumer goods and luxury items denied Americans during the War. With a background in sheet metal work he heard one recurrent theme- construction.

Charlie chatted with his girlfriend in Visitacion Valley. She expressed interest, and that's all it took for Charlie to detail his plans for the future. He saw growth, success and security from the rigors of the Depression era. He felt the confidence to carry out his plans. "Now it's time to start the business. Let me tell you what I have in mind."

Charlie dated Ceil Cull, an Irish Catholic nursing student, red hair and beautiful blue eyes, fiercely independent and ready to graduate from nursing school. Both their families lived in the Valley. She and Charlie discussed marriage, but neither decided yet. They faced their bright futures unencumbered. "Ceil, is your brother James interested in working?"

They sat on the steps of Ceil's parent's house. The clear San Francisco weather held up. "Why, how nice of you to ask. He's always looking for a job, and you know he's a hard worker. He mentioned you visited him on your train ride from New Orleans back to San Francisco. What do you have in mind?"

Charlie paced on the sidewalk. "If I can buy rolled sheet metal in bulk, I want to start a business and expand into large contracts. Heating and air conditioning will boom. I did my apprenticeship in sheet metal work. I have a lot of ideas for machines to do the work of ten men cutting and shaping in the shop. I could underbid the competition. Mechanization. Innovation. Efficiency. These will rule the next generation of successful businesses. But we'll always need men to install. It will be hard at first, but I'm a hard worker. I've got Josie's husband Benny Barazoto lined up. He introduced me to his friend, a very nice fellow named Eddie Salomone. That guy is an expert in architectural sheet metal. The three of us will make a go of it. Buildings are sprouting up all over the area. I don't see the boom slowing down. I'm going to start by building a home and go up from there."

Charlie started the business, planning, estimating and working like the devil. He bought a brand new car with his Navy pay and poker winnings during the War. He had the capital to buy tools.

The office posed a problem. Friends mentioned an inexpensive location. Charlie rented a garage in Visitacion Valley just down the street from Josie and Benny. The lower floor used to be a chicken coop. The partners learned to love that smell. To save a little more, the men asked Josie to take messages on her home phone, run down to the garage and wait till they discussed the situation. Then she ran back home and completed the calls.

*

Frank charged the boys rent while they stayed at home. After the war, Charlie and Dave moved out of the Teddy Street house. Frank stayed on, sticking to his routine of early rising, making wine, and work at PG+E. He never missed a day's work.

His children visited frequently. Frank enjoyed the company. He spent his free time in the garden, cultivating vegetables, fruit and flowers. He never lost his taste for wine or cigarettes.

-

A bit of a perfectionist, Charlie's reputation for excellence spread. He expanded into larger contracts and a larger office. In the early years after the War, the supply of sheet metal stayed tight. Charlie was at the bottom of the food chain when it came to suppliers. Work increased and the metal supply didn't. He faced a critical situation. Find enough to finish the present contracts, on time and at budget, or risk loosing the business and go under. His reputation and dreams depended on a successful outcome.

Many post-war businessmen in California failed.

Charlie discussed the options with Eddie. They picked the only one with a chance of success. Charlie approached a friend from the War, Mr. Jim Tuck, who owned an established sheet metal business called Atlas Heating. He set up an appointment.

Charlie sat in comfortable wooden chair in Atlas's front office. The noise of business didn't distract him from his request. "Mr. Tuck, I'm in trouble. I'll default on my contract if I don't secure more sheet metal. You know how tight the market is these days. Do you have any extra I can buy to get me through?"

"You're right, Charlie. Supplies are tight. I'd like to help. I'm glad you came to me."

"I'll be happy to return the favor just as soon as the supply loosens up. It's important."

Jim Tuck looked around. He knew first hand the hectic conditions in the construction industry. "How much do you need?"

Charlie decided against a poker face strategy. He spilled his guts, including the fact the business could go under. "I could loose everything."

"Charlie, I can see what a hard worker you are," Mr. Tuck replied. "Your future is bright. Don't forget me when the company is big and powerful. I'll deliver it this afternoon. I'm glad you came to me. I'm happy to help out."

True to his word, Mr. Tuck delivered any and all sorts of scrap sheet metal. Charlie, James, Benny and Eddie finished the contract on time without default.

Charlie returned the favor. He never forgot the kindness of his competitor. They developed into fast friends and business collaborators. "When I invent a labor-saving device, I'm going to name it after you, Jim. Thanks."

In 1947, Frank retired from PG+E. At his age, he couldn't work the hours any more.

Charlie dropped by his father's house on Teddy Street. Teddy Street looked different now. Quiet and empty.

The vigor disappeared.

Charlie had a few hours between construction jobs. He didn't want his father feeling lonely. His father sat in the kitchen, eating lunch, smoking, enjoying a little wine. Charlie saw Frank aging and living in the past. "Everything all right, dad?"

Frank smiled and turned towards the radio. He took a drag on his cigarette. "Charlie, nice to see you. Josie came yesterday and showed off her boy Ray. He's growing up nice. I like kids. When you have yours, bring them by. It's nice to see them. I can take them for a walk. Then I can give them back."

Charlie, confronted by his father's silence, blurted out his reason for the visit. "Dad, now that you're retired, it might be nice to visit the old country. See old relatives, check on your family. Dave, Josie and I will pay for the whole thing. can we send you on a trip to Italy?"

He finished off the pasta. "No, I left Italy because I didn't like it there. Why would I go back?"

"Josie thought you'd say that. She had another idea. We can set up a tour of America by train. When her boy Ray is out of school, he could go with you. You always talk about seeing Chicago and the other big cities. Will you do it?"

Frank sat a moment, puffing smoke rings. "Now that sounds like fun. You kids would do that for me?"

"We want to give you something like this."

Frank's eyes drooped. Always rising at dawn, Frank kept up the routine in retirement. He fixed coffee first, had breakfast later. After lunch a little nap. Then his walk downtown to speak Italian with the merchants. "Let's give it a try."

Charlie realized his father's afternoon nap approached. "I'm going back to work, dad. I'll arrange everything for the trip. It will be great fun. Goodbye, I'll see you soon."

Frank took the trip with Ray Barazoto, Josie's son. Grandfather and grandson traveled first class to the Midwest and the East coast. Ray sent postcards signed by them both. They enjoyed the time together.

After the train trip across America, Frank's health declined. Emphysema. Breathing problems. Loss of appetite. Josie volunteered to take him in.

It wasn't an easy thing for her to do. Frank tried to boss her around, let her do all the chores. Her two boys slept in the basement. Frank took the main bedroom upstairs. Josie endured the chore willingly. Life changed for the Barazoto's.

In 1956, Josie couldn't do any more nursing at her home. She had kids to raise. Frank moved to a nursing home, too sick to be on his own.

Charlie and Eddie Salamone became a duo when Benny dropped out of the company. He needed a job with less stress, now that Frank lived with him. The remaining partners decided on a bigger operation. Eddie was a whiz at estimating. Charlie picked the jobs, set bids and ordered material.

They moved their business, Valley Sheet Metal, to Hunter's Point in San Francisco. They hired more men and picked up the pace of bidding. With the growing population of California and the economy rising, business boomed. They moved into bigger and more expensive jobs. Stress increased, but so did the profits.

Charlie invented a new, innovative process to build and join sheets of metal roofing. With Jim Tuck in mind, he named the machine The Atlas. It made the company a lot of money. Jim Tuck appreciated Charlie's gesture, returning the favor of years past.

*

Charlie and Ceil sat outside her mother's house, alone on the steps. For privacy. He returned from the war three years ago. He'd dated long enough. He'd been told not to discuss marriage till Ceil graduated from nursing school. She had conditions. He wouldn't budge. Today, he was ready to compromise. "Will you marry me?"

She smiled, blue eyes gleaming, as Charlie rambled on and on. A sea breeze filled the air. Clouds outlined the Golden Gate. Finally, Ceil spoke. "Yes."

"Yes? You'll do it? Great." Charlie felt an equal mixture of relief and happiness. He couldn't see much except her face. Perspiration dripped down his brow into his eyes. This time they'd really do it. He had plans for that, too. "Ceil, I want a big Italian family, four boys and an equal number of girls."

Ceil hugged him. "You're a wonderful person. I'd be honored. Just as long as you remember there is more to life than work. And remember this, Charlie. The children will be half Irish."

On February twenty-seventh 1949 they were married at Our Lady of the Visitacion Catholic Church. Ceil almost cancelled the date again. She wouldn't walk down the aisle till Charlie agreed to one demand. They would raise their children in the Catholic religion.

He conceded that point.

The fashionably dressed crowd returned to her mother's house for the reception. Her brother James Cull kept bar, and her sister Mary played vinyl records on the victrola. Everyone danced. After hours of celebration, the couple slipped out to begin their honeymoon at a resort in Oakland. The next day they moved into Charlie's newly completed house in Millbrae.

-

Between water skiing, golf, and having children, their lives encompassed much more than work. Peggy, born in 1951, turned the parents outside themselves as they gave everything to their baby. Her birth also caused a new emphasis inward, on family. From the beginning, they invited guests for dinner. Friends, relatives, business contacts and acquaintances came to love and enjoy these meals at the Andrews. Without a crowd of ten or more, it seemed subdued. The opportunities for free ranging discussion opened up the wide outside world to everyone involved.

After Elaine came, maternal duties precluded a nursing career for Ceil. She concentrated on a loving home environment to nurture the children. The group swelled as Janet, Nancy and finally Mary arrived.

Their most memorable times came on holidays. One Christmas Ceil dressed them identically in hand made outfits. The picture brought joy to every visitor to the Andrews home. The girls built an active social life with their sisters, friends, and relatives. Ceil's sister Mary also had five children with her husband Guido, and as the decibel level rose, so did the fun. Family is important to those Italians Mary and Ceil married.

The children remembered the lessons learned on the sly during these family dinners. Adult values about hard work, careers and morals made their way into parental expectations. The girls took on their values. Everyone had a say, although they all understood their parents' positions. Charlie and Ceil remained a strong moral compass for their youngsters.

In September 1957 Charlie drove to the Millbrae Nursing Home to visit his father. The warm ocean breeze of the early fall day cooled him off from work.

Since his retirement, Frank's emphysema worsened. He never lost his taste for wine. Charlie visited frequently because Frank could no longer care for himself.

Charlie walked in to the cluttered room at the nursing home. "Dad, how are you today?"

He puffed his cigarette. "As good as I can expect."

Charlie saw a small, frail old man coughing at the table. His skin, usually the color of olives, looked shrunken and pale. He held the cigarette in one hand, a small glass of wine in the other. The place smelled of stale smoke. "What can I get you?"

"It's good to see you, son. Not so many visitors any more. What brings you by today?"

Charlie thought his father needed a little cheering up. He liked watching the kids, at least for a short time. "I got a big new contract for the Sutro Towers. It's about time we took another vacation. We could bring the kids. How about another train ride across country?"

"I'm a little tired."

"We'll take good care of you, dad."

Frank's body shook with cough. "Thanks for the offer, Charlie. I do love your kids. They make life worth living. Maybe some other time. My breathing isn't so good. You go ahead, use the money and take your kids. Congratulations on your new contract for the towers. You always were a hard worker."

"Dad, you taught me that."

"Good. At least I taught you something good."

Charlie looked at his father. Recently, he declined all invitations with some excuse. Today, though, Frank didn't look so good. "You want me to get you something, dad?"

He whispered. "No, Charlie, but next time, bring Peggy down to see me. I have something for her."

Charlie went to work. As the day sped towards closing time, he answered a call from the staff at the Millbrae Nursing Home.

The assistant administrator came on the line. "Charlie, it's your father. He's had some kind of attack. His breathing is poor. Can you come down right away?"

"I'll be there. Thanks for calling."

Speeding down the highway, Charlie remembered the morning's conversation and the look to his father's face. He found the nursing aide in the room. She stood beside the bed. "I'm sorry, Charlie, he's gone. It was peaceful. There was no pain."

Charlie looked at his father. He knew Frank had a full life. Losing a parent stung. Life would never be the same without Frank Andrews.

Charlie arranged the wake at the Vallento-Marini Funeral Parlor the next day, September eighth 1957. He and Ceil made calls to relatives and friends. Later that evening, the adults gathered at the wake.

"The funeral parlor did a nice job," Ceil commented to Josie.

The casket lay open. Charlie and Ceil, Josie and Benny, Dave and his wife Shirley attended. Eddie Salomone and his wife Inez dropped by and said a prayer. Frank's friend Sam Cuzenza stayed a long time. Sam spoke of the good old days when he and Frank arrived in San Francisco and ate outside at North Beach. Sam mentioned Frank's love of wine, and his dream to become a vintner. It was a small crowd for such a long life.

He was put to his final rest next to Elizabeth in Colma Cemetery, San Francisco. The gravestone reads Frank and Elizabeth Andrews. The family went home to mourn the loss of grandpa.

CHAPTER FIFTEEN

LIKE FATHER, LIKE DAUGHTER

Valley Sheet Metal, as Charlie called the company, grew by leaps and bounds.

One building at a time, Charlie and Eddie accumulated real estate. California accommodated them by thirsting for warehouses, offices, and manufacturing sites. They parlayed their expertise into further investments.

Eddie decided on early retirement. His golf game improved.

Charlie played a little, fished a lot, but his focus never wavered. Family, business, then fun and games. Between high-rise San Francisco buildings, the famous Sutro tower of Valley Sheet Metal, and his private real estate, Charlie's fortunes continued.

Charlie and Ceil put the last two kids through nursing school. There were bumps along the road, arguments and discussions. In the end, all five chose life enhancing, service careers. They understood it was time to give to the society and the family that nurtured them and gave them opportunities to succeed.

Holiday reunion at Thanksgiving substituted for their family dinners.

The day brought smiles and the aroma of good Italian food. Guests crowded into the kitchen, spilled into the living room. Children sat everywhere, from the floor to their parents' laps.

After the feast, Janet stood, eyes filled with tears. "We owe our father Charlie so much. Dad's war exploits made him a hero. Can you believe the courage he demonstrated for our country?"

One of Charlie's friends yelled, "Here here."

"You may have read the article in the San Francisco paper about veterans of World War II. Our veterans are dying at a rate of thirty thousand a year. We in the 'Baby Boomer' generation have an opportunity. We owe them our life and our liberty. Before it's too late, we should take the opportunity to thank dad and others like him. We can follow the lead of President Kennedy, who went out of his way to visit military personnel. He credited the thoughts in a poem as his inspiration. He would not allow it to become reality. I kept a copy from the article."

> *God and the soldier all men adore,*
> *In time of danger and no more,*
> *For when the danger is past and all things righted,*
> *God is forgotten and the old soldier slighted.(13)*

"Thank you for that, Janet."

Charlie stood before the throng, friends and family ranging from infants to eighty. "I'm happy to see everyone, and I mean everyone this Thanksgiving. You may not believe it, but we miss the girls. We are proud of their accomplishments."

Ceil announced, "A toast to the girls."

Charlie raised his hands. "Peggy has a busy Nurse Practitioner practice. Elaine recently started her private practice of law in Anchorage. Janet is now the official family dentist. Nancy is starting her nursing career. And last but not least, Mary will graduate from the University of Colorado School of Nursing."

Peggy the eldest stood. "Thanks, dad. We owe it all to you for saying things like, 'If you think I'm going to work every day to support you kids lying around the swimming pool all summer, you are in for a rude awakening!' I recall a special time when I first realized how much I loved him. I was twelve. We traveled to northern California for the pheasant-hunting season. I'll never forget how good it felt, just dad and I and no other kids. It's one of the few times I had him all to myself, sloshing around in a cold wet field looking for birds so he could shoot them. I cared nothing about birds or hunting, just about dad. That night he and the men discussed teenagers at dinner. They acted like I wasn't there. One of dad's friends said I would grow up, get married and have kids. Dad corrected the men. 'No, not my daughter. She will be very successful. She'll go to college and have a career and be a success.' I did do that, and I'll never forget his faith in me."

Applause filled the home on the Peninsula south of San Francisco. Charlie gazed out on the San Francisco Bay, a smile on his face.

Elaine stood, the ringleader of the group. "Before the party breaks up, we have a little entertainment. I planned to sing the aria from the Italian opera *La Figaro*, but I have a sore throat. So, without further ado, here's our alternate plan. We call this a day in the life of the Andrews family."

Peggy and Nancy, dressed in traditional golf clothes consisting of pink short shorts, wide brimmed Mexican hat, oversized golf shoes and children's length drivers, strode into the living room. Before they rolled over laughing, they demonstrated the modern components of the golf swing, nearly taking out a lamp in the process.

"And now for scene two, ladies and gentlemen, a rendition of Charlie at work."

Elaine, wearing white shirt and blue work pants, sat at the desk. "What do you mean, not ready?! The contract calls for Tuesday."

Her voice rose to a scream. "I don't care if your truck is broken. I want that part on Tuesday. I hired a helicopter to lift it to the roof on Tuesday. I don't want to take tourists on sightseeing trips on Tuesday, so," voice dripping with sugar, "I want the part Tuesday. Thank you, I'll see you then. Pleasure doing business with you." Mopping her brow, she smiled and took a bow.

For the third act, Mary and Janet demonstrated a typical Andrews' family vacation. Janet, burdened by tennis racquet, snorkel, beach towel and four hundred——page novel, entered stage left. Mary, with roller blades, badminton racquet and fishing pole, follow behind.

Janet said, "For months now, I looked forward to catching up with my sisters, playing with my nephews and nieces, and getting back in tennis shape. Isn't this great?"

"I'm exhausted," Mary replied. "If I get up at five AM to run, then eat a quick breakfast, I can make the boat for water skiing. But then I miss golf. In the afternoon, it's badminton and tennis and nature walks. I can't go to bed till midnight or I'll miss out on the chatter. I love vacation!"

After the applause died down, Elaine stood for an announcement. "This is the last Andrews sisters' show. We're getting too old to perform. Besides, we're tired of being mistaken for the singing Andrews Sisters. From now on, we'll let the next generation take over. They have more energy."

The dinner party broke into pockets of conversation. Elaine said, "There is another part of World War II history I've been reading about. After fifty years of cover-up, facts of a congressional investigation disseminated the truth about Italians and World War II. *Una Storia Segreta,* The Secret Story traced the U.S. government's mistreatment of Italians during World War II. Within three months of the attack on Pearl Harbor, new rules striped many Italians of their constitutional rights. Italian—American citizens lost their civil rights, jobs, property and income.

"Unlike the Japanese—American story, this part of our war effort remained secret till Representative Rick Lazio of New York spoke in Congress. 'Many are not aware of it because their parents and grandparents didn't want to talk about it. They were ashamed of it.'

Over ten thousand Italian-Americans bore this discrimination and mistreatment. One family was the famous DiMaggio family of San Francisco. Dominic and Joe played professional baseball. Dom DiMaggio served in the US Navy in 1942. His father, Guiseppe, a citizen of the United States, was forbidden to fish and go near Joe DiMaggio's restaurant on Fisherman's Wharf, San Francisco. The reason? Guiseppe was Italian, labeled an undesirable alien.

"Congress demanded a Justice Department report. The Italian leaders didn't want money or compensation. They required an acknowledgement that this racial discrimination took place. They wish for discrimination in all forms to stop." (14)

After the dinner, the family discussed a method to pass their good fortune to the next generation. The five acting Andrews sisters decided on a gift. They all graduated from Mercy High School, a private Catholic institution. Their educational experience as well as the discipline and focus instilled by the Sisters deserved recognition. Reaching out to those not able to afford a private school, but who wished the discipline and college preparatory education Mercy offered, the Andrews sisters collaborate on a scholarship fund. Each year, a new student is awarded tuition from their fund. Without it, the student could not otherwise attend Mercy. Letters of thanks from the scholarship recipients prove their success.

A

CHAPTER SIXTEEN

NEW WORLD MEETS OLD

High over the Atlantic- So many traumas, with Marcello's bitter departure, the abandonment of babies by Rosaria and Marcello, and Rosaria's suicide. Would the circle of genealogy remain broken?

As the flight neared Roma, the family burst with nervous energy. In an effort to relax, Janet reviewed the obstacles to tracking her relatives. "I turned to a professional for help. George Ott of Heritage Consulting and Services specialized in genealogy. He helped hundreds of families like ours trace their ancestry."

Peggy asked, "What caused the breakthrough?"

"George figured there might be citizenship or Social Security or Selective Service records from Marcello's San Francisco days. Everyone in the US age fifteen to sixty regardless of nationality had to fill out a government registration card. He found the old World War I Selective Service registration records. Marcello's card, handwritten and yellow with age, revealed he came from Salandra, Italy, in the region of Basilicata."

Elaine said, "That pinpointed the Italian branch. How did you find the Vineland branch?"

Janet said, "I mentioned our first trip to Italy. A friendly man approached me in the piazza of Salandra. 'I know about the Onorato's.' I asked his name. 'I am Vincenzo Cashio. My grandmother was the sister of your grandmother. You seek your grandfather's relatives. I'm from your grandmother's side.'

"The entire family eventually moved to Vineland, New Jersey. Everybody in Salandra knew it as an Italian colony in America. I visited Vineland twice to meet our relatives there and research Donata's gravesite. George found legal papers concerning the lost relatives. They led to other discoveries and a wealth of information. The papers documented the divorce of Rosaria and Pasquale Iurlaro in Vineland, after she ran away with Marcello."

As the jet descending towards Roma, Janet worried about the effects this trip might have on her father. She remembered the picture of father, uncle and aunt taken the day after Elizabeth's suicide. "The picture disturbed me. It explained much about events since that awful day. Elizabeth suffered terrible depression. Was there meaning to her suffering?"

Peggy gripped her sister's hand as she cried.

"Learning of Grandma's suicide gave me the opportunity to review my own life. Since my illness, therapy and recovery, I wonder about the meaning of breast cancer to my life. My sisters, you always listened and shared your ideas. My husband Dave helped me evaluate all the advice and opinions we gathered. My 'survivors' group at Stanford University became so much more than support. We became friends and confidants. I integrated the fact of cancer into my life.

"Breast cancer gave me an intense sense of purpose. After that wakeup call, I know myself better. I certainly know my friends, the ones that stood by me through the ordeal. After a hard look at my life, I asked the question, 'have I done all I want?' That is when I became passionate to discover my family. After all, how much time did I have?"

The plane touched down.

Waiting at the crowded Rome airport, Sandra their interpreter met the family with a mini-van. "It's several hours to Salandra, just enough time to catch up and practice our Italian."

She, Elaine, Peggy and Janet chatted in animated Italian. The rest napped to ameliorate jet lag.

Elaine said, "This meeting in Salandra makes me more nervous by the minute. God only knows what else we'll find out about our family. I hope we learn something unique and good."

Approaching the mountainous 578 road, the countryside changed. The fields and vineyards grew on steep hills. They drove through foothills past Potenza, chief city of the Basilicata region. Continuing upward, they passed Calciano and made a right turn.

"That's Salandra, at the end of this road," Sandra announced. "Get ready for a great experience."

The Andrews family peered out the van windows, silent. A quarter-mile before the city limits on the Autostrada outside Salandra, a car honked its horn. Three Italians stood outside. A boy waved a picture of the American flag. His parents stood by, crying and grasping the boy's shoulders.

Janet burst into tears. "Stop the car. That's Domenico Annunziata, our relative!"

On the side of the road, overlooking olive trees, sheep and green pastures, the Andrews approached the little Fiat. Janet led the charge.

A crying Domenico Rocco Annunziata ran towards them, speaking Italian. *"Buono sera, signorina.* I couldn't wait. My wife and I sat in the car for the last half—hour anticipating your arrival. Welcome to Salandra!"

In the chill wind, Domenico's cheeks ran with tears as he hugged Janet. "Hello, I'm Domenico. Mariangela, sister to your grandfather, was my grandmother. This is my wife Maria. She will have to talk to you, I'm too emotional."

Janet spoke in passable Italian. *"Le presento Signor* Charles Andrews, my father. He is Marcello's son."

Hugs and kisses took the place of words to convey their joy. The five sisters and their parents bonded with lost Italian relatives.

Their breath and some order returned. After drying their eyes, the families mingled, murmuring expressions of love in two languages. Domenico waved his hands to be understood. "Please, I forget myself. You must follow us, *adesso.* There are others of your family to meet. They want to see you very badly. *E molto importante.*"

They left the vehicles in the cobble—stoned piazza of Salandra. The brisk morning air stimulated them as they walked down a medieval street. They turned into a narrow alley between buildings. Domenico led them along another, smaller street till he stopped and gestured up.

Before them stood a two story, whitewashed structure, fragrant with history. "This is the family house. I'm afraid we have more family to meet. *Avanti, avanti.*"

Mariangela D'Alessandro, Marcello's sister, lived there in her later years. They filed up the stairs, one by one entering the overcrowded home.

Domenico's wife Marie waited for all to arrive. She announced, "Mr. Andrews, here are your cousins."

As they sat in the comfortably furnished room, sweaters tight to ward off cold, two elderly gentlemen emerged from the kitchen. Shorter than Charlie's five foot six height, the gentlemen possessed the same skin color, build, and facial features. The three astonished men shook hands.

"This is Giovanni Annunziata," Sandra said, touching the older, clean shaved gentleman. "He gives you his love and gratitude for coming to visit. And this is Luigi Annunziata," pointing to the slightly younger man with a moustache. "He wishes you his best. You are first cousins. Meeting together like this, it's beautiful!"

Charlie, usually never at a loss for words, dried his eyes. "Thank you for asking us to visit your village and your home. You are all so kind to perfect strangers. Thank you."

Giovanni took Charlie's hand in his. "Not strangers. Family. Whatever is ours is yours. You are welcome to be here and stay here. Our home is your home."

The Annunziata's home hosted the reunion. They gave a tour, starting in the basement. Hand made sausage and cheese hung on racks for storage. The living quarters were modern, though small. Cooking utensils of every shape and form crowded the kitchen, birthplace to the coming feast. Upstairs, Domenico showed them the bedroom of their grandmother, Mariangela, Marcello's sister. Memorabilia illustrated her life and times. All the intricate familial relationships were finally deciphered.

The group gathered around the kitchen table for a demonstration. In their honor, the oldest and most experienced cook made pasta the old way, by hand. Ritualistically, she gathered flour, eggs and water along with the mixing instruments, and placed them on the wooden chopping block work-table. Into a molded heap of flour she broke several eggs. While mixing the flour and eggs by hand, her assistant added sips of water to obtain the proper consistency. This mixing stage continued till the little pile of flour disappeared and was transformed into the raw material.

With practiced repetitive motion, the elderly grandmother pulled and separated, pulled and separated. Adding water as needed, the pulls became longer and longer, the strands thinner. Longer still, until she removed a portion. This she continued to work on, till each strand took the same appearance, long, flat, and uniform. In stages, she moved to the next section and the next, till finally lay an orderly pile of linguini, enough to feed them all. Elaine initiated the applause. She offered a toast in Italian to the prowess and concentration necessary to complete such a task.

The cook smiled and said, "Wait till you taste it."

Dinner proved to be a feast of original Italian recipes and products. They conversed throughout the evening. *Mangiare!*

At a late hour, exhausted, the Andrews left for a brief rest.

The next morning, the clan drove in a convoy to the church for Mass.

"I cried so much, but I feel great today," Janet said. "They're such wonderful people. Dad, what did you think when you met your cousins?"

"Surprised. I thought they broke the mold when they made me, but now I see I have two twins."

"I'm so impressed with Domenico," Janet continued. "He is so young and handsome. Maria his wife is the cutest, most sociable gal. She always has the right word for the situation. I wonder if Domenico cries this much when we're not around."

"Everyone enjoyed yesterday," Peggy said. "Domenico feels so strongly about us. Did you see how his face lit up when we met his kids, Luigi and Felice? They're adorable! And those pictures they made to greet us, what a touching gesture."

The old church shone as new voices rose in prayer. The priest made special mention of the visitors from America and the story of persistence, family and love that prompted the visit. They walked to the altar and shared wine and bread, transformed into the body and blood of Christ.

The Andrews picked this time to repay the kindness. "We've arranged for the meal today," Charlie said. "Please join us in celebrating this reunion. We've been looking forward to this for many months."

At the entrance of the banquet hall, yet another surprise visitor awaited. A short, black haired women dressed in a traditional black jacket and long skirt. "This is Guiseppina Annunziata," Sandra translated, "your cousin."

The Andrews commented that Guiseppina looked just like Mariangela. The newly reunited relatives dissolved into traditional tears.

As they filed in, seven from the Andrews family and twice the number of Italian relatives, antipasto spread over the long, narrow table outfitted with candles and tablecloth. The bouquet of light red wine filled the room. Sunlight from picture windows outlined the fields below. A mixture of hand gestures, a little English and much Italian brought the noise level to a new height.

Maria Annunziata tapped her glass. "We here in the Old Country wish to welcome our new family from the New World. Family is very important to us here. We now see that family is equally important to our relatives from across the sea. I pray we remain together in good health and vitality. To the Andrews family, a toast."

The seating arrangement intermingled the families. The parish priest led them in a prayer before the meal.

With a breathtaking onset of smells, waiters served the first course of fish. Conversation continued between elders and children, Americans and

Italians. Pasta and another wine appeared.

Emotions of the years, not yet spent over the last days of discovery, burst forth, especially for Domenico. He filled his conversation with praise for his relatives. He understood the perseverance necessary for the Andrews to track them down and arrange the reunion.

As the waiters brought dessert, Charlie tapped his glass. The room quieted. Standing with Ceil, holding hands, he struggled to speak. "We can't say how you lovely people have affected us. I didn't set my expectations too high, for fear of being let down. It's my American caution. But as I discussed with my wife last night, I've been so moved. Poor Domenico, he's crying already!"

handkerchiefs waved about the room. Maria wiped Domenico's face.

"Thank you, Domenico and Maria for taking us in and showing us your home. We truly feel as welcome as your own family. *Grazie tante. Molto gentile."*

He paused to sip his water, letting his roiling emotions subside. "Last night, Ceil and I discussed our plans. We decided our plans must include you, our family here in Italy. I would like to invite you, our friends and family from Salandra to visit us in the United States. Let's call it an extended family reunion. Stay with us. Visit our homes. Before you leave our home, you will be our family. We have several generations of stories to tell!"

Domenico answered for all the Italian relatives. Arms extended, with a big smile, he shouted, "Yes!"

Charlie posed with Giovanni and the mustached Luigi, with Guiseppina Annunziata, all of Mariangela's remaining relatives. Next, Domenico, his brother Vincenzo, and their sisters Mariangela and Orsola posed next to the Andrews family. With the wide-angle lens they took everyone together. A truly international family portrait. Charlie and Ceil, flanked by their children, along with Vincenzo's family and the families of Mariangela, Domenico and Orsola.

Everyone hugged. Domenico promised to visit the USA. He stood silently, tears falling from his cheeks, as the mini-van pulled away from the village of Salandra, tires creaking on the cobblestones, tears distorting the visibility.

"Arrivederci," shouted the Andrews family one last time.
"Ciao!"

A

CHAPTER SEVENTEEN

MARCELLO'S CHILDREN

Josie, Josephina Barazoto, the oldest child of Marcello and Rosaria, died in 2000. She lived long enough to celebrate the Italian relatives visit to California.

Dave Andrews, the youngest, died tragically of lung cancer. His wife and two daughters survive him, near the nest just south of San Francisco. He and Charlie had a rocky relationship that lasted for years.

After Dave's diagnosis of lung cancer, the brothers mellowed. Two years prior to Dave's death, Charlie discussed selling his fishing boat. The equipment malfunctioned. It was too hard to navigate outside the Golden Gate. The fish wouldn't bite. The family dissuaded him. "One more season, dad. Just one more."

That year Dave and Charlie mended their fences. They fished regularly. It no longer mattered how many salmon struck the hook. After rising early, the brothers drove to the boat and spent the day sharing their love of the sea. They talked about old times. They enjoyed each other's company. The fish were an added attraction. As the season closed, Dave weakened. Finally, he succumbed to the tumor. After his death, Charlie decided it was time to part with the boat. He didn't need it any more.

Charlie and Ceil live in a temporarily empty nest. They fill their time with golf, business, and telephone calls to far flung relatives and friends.

Of the children of Marcello and Donata in Vineland, Virginia the youngest is alive and well. Born in 1915, the same year Marcello became a citizen, her life changed because of Donata's deathbed wish that her family remain together.

After Marcello and Rosaria abandoned the family in 1917, Donata asked nine-year-old Margharita to keep the family together and watch out for the young siblings. Everyone save Rocco and Margharita went to foster care at Saint Michael's orphanage in Hopewell, New Jersey.

A childless Italian couple adopted Virginia, an infant that year. Her new parents returned to Italy. Elizabeth, the next youngest, was also adopted. The other four siblings spent their youth growing up in Saint Michael's orphanage.

In 1931, Margharita, the eldest, married and known as Margaret Nocco, visited the orphanage at Saint Michael's on a nostalgic quest. She spoke to Sister Mary Edigna about her long search for her siblings. She explained Donata's deathbed wish.

Sister Edigna remembered the children and told Mrs. Margaret Nocco where they had been taken. Three days later, the elderly Sister died.

Margaret remembered, "If I hadn't seen her then I might never have found my sisters."(15)

Elizabeth, living in Perth Amboy, New Jersey, was traced to Woodbridge High School. Records indicated her address and Margaret found her. They celebrated their reunion.

Only one sibling remained lost.

Finding Virginia proved a challenge. Her foster parents had moved to Matawan, NJ. Margaret Nocco located Virginia's foster-brothers in Matawan. The adoptive parents, Mr. and Mrs. Angelo Pirozzi, took the young Virginia to Naples years before.

Virginia had every reason to believe she was a native Italian. Margaret Nocco didn't surprise her sister with a letter, because Virginia hadn't known of the adoption. It wasn't until she applied for a marriage certificate in Italy that she learned her real last name. She wrote to Vineland in 1937 and contacted Margaret. They kept up a correspondence that lasted through World War II.

After the War, economic conditions in Italy deteriorated. Recession and farming collapse caused the loss of millions of jobs. Famine returned. After years of entreaties from Margaret Nocco, Virginia consented to immigrate with her husband to the USA.

Legalities threatened to abort the reunion. Though Virginia was considered a citizen of the US by birth, her husband was not, according to Italian law. Margaret interceded with the US consul. During the prolonged legal battle, she never gave up. She remembered her mother's last wish.

In 1949 Virginia and her husband sailed for the USA.

Margaret waited on the dock in Hoboken, NJ, just yards from where the *Rotterdam* delivered Marcello to the New World. She traveled with an entourage: Elizabeth and her husband; a brother; another sister; her half-brother; and Virginia's foster brothers.

After an unbearable wait, the ship docked. As the passengers debarked, Margaret searched their eyes.

The similarity couldn't be mistaken. They rushed to each other in a storm of tears. Virginia returned home, reunited after thirty-two years.

The sisters reminisced and shed tears of joy for days. Virginia's arrival fulfilled Donata's dying wish. The youngest sister praised Margaret's persistence and perseverance.

Margaret found a home for Virginia in Perth Amboy and a job for her husband at the local copper plant. They became best of friends. Margaret said, "I prayed every night for this and it's like a dream. You know, life is good." (15)

Virginia echoes that sentiment from her home in Vineland. She lives alone, and loves visitors.

In 2001, Charles Andrews and his daughters flew in for a visit.

The octogenarians sat formally in Virginia's living room. Relatives from throughout the Vineland area dropped by. Soon, the ice thawed and stories began. Virginia said, "Come here, brother. Sit next to me."

With respect, Charlie recollected his memories of Marcello, their father.

Virginia nodded. She had been too small to remember him. She contributed stories of the D'Alessandro family and Margharita's quest to reunite all of Donata's children.

Brother and sister commiserated that their children grew too fast. They agreed that having grandchildren was easier.

Virginia, Charlie and the relatives ate, cried, and reveled in their shared heritage. As the evening drew to a close, they bid each other farewell, knowing their first meeting might be their last.

Life is good. For Italians, family is of utmost importance. The D'Alessandro's felt that way about their new extended family.

For Janet, the circle finally felt unbroken.

FOOTNOTES

1. Quoted in *An Album of the Great Wave of Immigration*, by April Koral, page 7, from the Ellis Island Immigration Museum, Ellis Island, NYC
2. Dino Coltro in *La Cucina Tradizionale Veneta*.
3. Quoted in *An Album of the Great Wave of Migration*, p. 24, from the Ellis Island Immigration Museum, Ellis Island, NYC; by Elda Willitts from Lucca, Italy
4. Quoted in Daniels, Roger; *Coming to America- A History of Immigration and Ethnicity*, page 187
5. Quoted in *Ethnic Americans* by David Reimers and Leonard Dinnerstein
6. Quoted in Gambino, Richard; *Blood of My Blood*, Doubleday and Company, Garden City, NY, 1974, page 71
7. Quoted in DeConde, Alexander; *Half Bitter, Half Sweet- An Excursion into Italian American History*. NY, Charles Scribner's Son's, 1971, page 86
8. March, 1875, L'Eco d'Italia article
9. Autobiography of Charles K. Landis, Vineland Historical Society, Vineland, NJ
10. Transcript of divorce decree, Pasquale Iurlaro
11. Transcript of divorce decree, Pasquale Iurlaro
12. Birth certificate, Charles Andrews
13. Denver Post article by Dr. Lawrence Hergott
14. Gazette-Telegraph article by Gannett News Service
15. Newspaper article featuring the reunion of the D'Alessandro family
16. Material for chapter Thirteen, the Merchant Marine, from the *Jeremiah O'Brien*. An original Liberty Ship, it now functions as a working history museum. Staffed by volunteers, its home base is San Francisco's Fisherman's Warf.

TO ORDER
A TRIO OF LIES

Discounts are available for quantities over nine.
Shipping is included with pre-paid orders.
Send payment in full for FREE SHIPPING   to
Pikes Peak Publishing
2130 Hollowbrook, #100
Colorado Springs, CO 80918
Master Card or
Visa (please circle one)
· Specify name on card
NAME_____
NUMBER_____
EXPIRATION DATE_____
CIRCLE METHOD OF PAYMENT CHECK
CREDIT CARD MONEY ORDER

RATES
1 TO 9 COPIES @ $16.99 PER COPY
10 OR GREATER @ $15.00 PER COPY
EXPECT DELIVERY IN ONE WEEK
TOTAL_____

ORDER BY EMAIL FOR CASH ON DELIVERY
SERVICE
fjbarry@pol.net
INFORMATION ON THE WEB AT
WWW.FJBARRYMD.COM
Please, use this form for orders. Copy one for your
friends, relatives and loved ones.